MULTICULTURAL GUIDE TO CAREGIVING

Angelica Herrera Venson, DrPH

Absolute Author
Publishing House

Multicultural Guide to Caregiving
Copyright © 2021 by Angelica P. Herrera Venson, DrPH
All rights reserved.

Publisher: Absolute Author Publishing House
Editor: Dr. Melissa Caudle
Junior Editor: Paul S. Dupre

Paperback ISBN: 978-1-64953-320-3
eBook ISBN: 978-1-64953-321-0

Contents

Acknowledgments

This book is dedicated to my mom, Marisela Herrera, who epitomizes the self-sacrifice you see from caregivers in every sense of the word. I wish to thank Cassie Greenfield, MS, my incredible colleague, a scientist, and former caregiver, for her dedication to the Kapok Aging and Caregiver Resource website since its inception in 2014 and critical review and contributions to this book. To my sisters, Sylvia and Norma Herrera, as well as Lola Ortiz for their guidance and having an eye towards the authenticity of this book. Lastly, I'd be remiss if I didn't recognize the many mentors who shaped my understanding of aging and caregiving and turned me into the skeptical researcher I am today.

Chapter 1

My Connections with Caregiving

During my twenty-plus years of working in public health and gerontology (the study of aging and its related social, cultural, psychological, and biological aspects of aging), I have witnessed the challenges immigrant families face when trying to survive in a new land. These challenges could be anything from managing their kids' schooling to understanding our perplexing healthcare system or, as I fondly remember, getting lost across town until figuring out the public transportation system or walking from the grocery store with twenty bags in hand. My parents had their share of economic struggles as they tried to build a better life for my two sisters and me, navigating a new system with limited language skills. This system can quickly become overwhelming.

These challenges and sacrifices can be especially apparent when caring for and performing the duties of a primary caretaker for ailing and aging family members. Such challenges can get worse as the health of the care recipient deteriorates. Today, it's my mother who is growing weary as she cares for my dad, who was diagnosed with Alzheimer's disease in 2000. My sisters and I provide backup support to her, though only my older sister, Sylvia, lives in the same city. No doubt, Sylvia shoulders the greatest burden as the sibling in closest proximity to my folks. As I am editing this chapter now, she is on her way to take my parents for their COVID-19 vaccine. My other sister, Norma, and I had the fun job of getting them an appointment online after refreshing the pages about a thousand times. That's teamwork!

Now in my forties, especially as I juggle caring for a child with type 1 diabetes, I empathize with caregivers' struggles like my mom faces. I understand the time commitment, the financial burden, and most importantly, I feel their emotional toll. Like many of you reading this book, I'm in the "sandwich generation," a generation caring for the needs of those younger and older than me. This sandwich generation must balance the challenging tasks of managing child-rearing and taking care of older relatives or parents.

You'll read many references to my own Mexican heritage and cultural traditions. However, I know that these experiences will resonate with many minority and immigrant caregivers facing similar dual realities and conflicting norms.

A Special Type of Person

After my time working on the frontline in the community and witnessing the caregivers in my family, I am convinced that it takes a special person to be a good caregiver or at least a well-intentioned one. As a young person growing up on both sides of the U.S.-Mexico border in San Diego, I was surrounded by family members who selflessly cared for aging and sick loved ones. It set the standard for what caregiving means. Often, this care was provided with little or no practical or financial help from other siblings or family members. I saw first-hand as my parents cared for my dad's aging parents. They were flooded with medical bills and endless medical appointments. When my uncle got sick, they literally gave up their bed to provide post-surgery care for him. These prior experiences with caregiving planted the seed for my future career aspirations in aging and caregiving.

Although technically I was born in the U.S., my formative years were driven from the perspective of an immigrant child. My family and I regularly crossed the border into Mexico for family visits. Back in the 1980s, the border crossings were more fluid and less politically charged than today. We didn't have the massive border crossing infrastructure you see now with hundreds of cameras, constant car searches, or detection dogs circling your car at each crossing. Our visits to Tijuana (TJ) included stops at my grandma's house and street tacos, of course. My dad also snuck in a haircut and did so until his dementia prevented that regular experience. He also frequented the *Hipodromo* to bet on dog races, until my mom threatened to report him to child welfare services for neglecting to finance the basics, like food for his children.

I was in college when my dad took my salvaged junky car to get fixed across the border with one of his buddies for a discount. Only to get hounded by border patrol and taken into custody before they recognized my dad was completely innocent. My car apparently once belonged to a drug dealer and had hidden compartments. That explains the great deal I got on it at the auction! We lived so close to the border that kids living in Mexico were bussed from the border to my junior high and high schools. My family had scarce economic resources, but the caregiving showed me that my family was wealthy with love, dedication, and compassion.

When I left home to pursue my studies and began working in the community, I could see the same care and love among other families. I interviewed Mexican-American caregivers as part of my dissertation study and further research that followed in the next decade. The stories from those caregivers are forever ingrained in my head. My 'study subjects,' as we say in academia, were immensely resilient. I recall walking into one of the family's homes and noticing that it resembled a nursing home. The hallway was filled with wheelchairs and walkers, while the living room was packed with toys for their kids. The couple had taken in not just one, but both sets of parents into their home to care for them. I had another family whose matriarch had cared for her daughter-in-law as she slowly passed away from cancer. That same matriarch then cared for her wheelchair-bound husband with type 2 diabetes while caring for their adult son with schizophrenia. I was a starving student then and convinced my local Walmart to fund part of my research. I used that money to buy gift cards to reimburse them for their time, but if I could go back in time, I would shower those families with many riches.

With this spirit of caring and compassion, I am writing this book to pass on my experiences working in such a rewarding field. As a Mexican-American woman raised along the U.S.-Mexico border in a Filipino neighborhood and married to an African-American man, I bring you my perspective for tackling the hardships of caregiving as a person of color. My goal is to share the knowledge I have gained over the years with all your family caregivers and the next generation of public health advocates and gerontologists. I learned many important lessons during my academic training, fieldwork, and career, but one lesson I really understood is that we all will begin the aging process in our lives.

After we are born into this world, we grow, and inevitably experience a decline in our basic functions, some more than others. It is this shared human experience that connects and unites us all. I think the global readers of my website, *Kapok Aging and Caregiver Resources,* would agree that we all share this bond and, regardless of culture, that we care about our loved ones. Perhaps this bond of humanity caregivers share is why publishing on caregiving is primarily mainstream. Many of the books out there don't speak to the heart and soul of immigrant caregivers or the cultural norms and unique issues we face. To this day, one of our most-read articles touches on Ethiopians' experiences with caregiving. We are also not surprised at the growth in traffic from India, as more Indian-American families are grappling with caregiving across borders and seas and navigating conflicts between two sets of cultural norms.

The research and knowledge I have gained over the years form the basis of this book. This book is meant to be both educational and inspirational. Educational in the sense that no matter your age, you can still learn and gain new knowledge to improve the quality of your own golden years or those of an elder you are caring for and inspirational in the sense that this book will show that you can enjoy your retirement years. You're not the first, and you will not be the last to look for a better retirement or to have to juggle caregiving during that stage of life. There are so many resources out there, and if you put the time in to find them and learn about them, they can have endless returns.

We will delve into topics, such as how to stay afloat financially while caring for aging relatives, along with ways to approach those conflicts arising from culturally rooted traditions and expectations around eldercare while trying to live the American dream. We'll also make sure you receive the essentials about staying mentally grounded, how to go about finding the right caregiver resources, and the best practices we've learned to keep your loved ones and yourself in good health.

Witnessing Acts of Care and Love

Often, the only care and compassion from a dedicated family caregiver, a familiar face, can help family members stand up to the challenges of the coming day. Everyone's activities of daily living, or ADL, gradually decline as they age. Getting out of bed, bathing, cooking, or cleaning often requires patience from a caregiver to help the elder get through these tasks with some dignity.

Many of these caregivers compromise their own physical health, financial resources, and future job advancement to provide compassionate care to their family's elders. Caregivers often become stressed because of their increased workload and can also become emotionally burned out. This only adds additional stress to other areas of their lives and reduces their time to manage their own nuclear family.

I observed the love and sacrifice for family from my parents and family members. Caring for aging relatives was always in the backdrop of our family life. My parents were caregivers or provided support to many of my dad's relatives throughout their lives, including my Aunt Chelo, my dad's oldest sibling and the only female of nine children. As Aunt Chelo aged, she developed Alzheimer's disease and showed signs of paranoia, accusing others of stealing her money. One very memorable incident involved Aunt Chelo wandering away from home on her own. My sister, Sylvia, led a search for her, and eventually, the police found and sent her to the hospital. My parents were her unofficial guardians and took responsibility for every aspect of her care, from her laundry and doctor appointments to her finances.

Sadly, Aunt Chelo passed away in 2009. Few of my father's other siblings had made a presence in recent years or during those last moments before her passing. At her funeral, my mom stood and didn't mince her words. She delivered a loud and resentful repudiation of the family, denouncing all those family members for daring to show their faces at the funeral services while being absent in my aunt's life for the past decade when she really needed them. As recently as last month, I let my friend vent concerning the lack of involvement of her brothers and sisters in her parents' care, referring to them as 'buenos para nada' (good for nothings) and other unflattering appraisals. This sentiment from abandoned caregivers is all too common, leading to strained family relations.

My paternal grandmother was also cared for by my parents. My mom would take her to her medical appointments to monitor and treat her type 2 diabetes and other conditions. My mom told me just a few weeks before she passed away, she had gestured to her, pointing up to the heavens, insisting that she was ready for the Good Lord to take her. After one hospitalization, my grandmother was recovering in a skilled nursing facility (SNF). She then had a heart attack, and the medical team that responded resuscitated my ninety-six-year-old grandmother, but she was too far gone. My parents eventually made the heart-wrenching decision to "pull the plug," but did so knowing that it is what she had clearly wanted. I can't imagine the emotional toll this took on my parents. The care and support family didn't end there.

My parents also supported my Uncle Roberto, who was an extreme alcoholic and often in and out of the hospital because of his addiction. Uncle Roberto's wife was working multiple jobs, taking care of their children, and doing what she could to take care of her husband. My uncle was a U.S. citizen, who worked in the U.S., but lived across the border in Mexico. My parents lent their home in the U.S. so that he could have physical therapy visits with a therapist. I fondly remember my uncle as the jolly man who would dress up as Santa Claus on Christmas at my grandmother's house and distribute gifts. As kids, we weren't fully aware that some of that jolly was fueled by a six-pack. Unfortunately, my uncle passed away at a young age in his 40s because of his addiction.

When the Tables Turn

My mom helped as much as she could with my dad's family even as she noticed my dad's health decline. She then turned her attention to caring for him. My dad was diagnosed with Alzheimer's in 2000, and then our family noticed the mental changes that come with it, including memory loss and an inability to keep up with conversations. As some of you understand, it's a constant struggle between trying to help your loved ones retain as much independence as possible for the sake of their own sense of self-worth and confidence, but all the while wondering when it's time to step in and take over. I distinctly remember one memorable incident when my dad got so lost, he drove across the Mexican border where he hadn't gone in years. Thanks to my sister, some dedicated cousins on both sides of the border, the border patrol, and a GPS my sister had installed in his car, he was tracked down and made it back safely. It's not uncommon for people with dementia to revert to old memories. He may have been recalling the times when he lived in Mexico and headed south.

Before this incident, my dad had occasionally gone out for a drive and not returned for hours. Those occasions were the reason that my sister had secretly placed a GPS tracker on the car. After the border crossing incident, my sisters and I discussed and agreed that I would write a letter to the DMV describing his condition and recommending his driving license be revoked. My mom was torn about taking this measure, but we proceeded anyway. The DMV sent his doctor a form, which his doctor signed after having heard about the incident. It worked, and my dad's license was revoked. It wasn't anything to celebrate, but it was necessary. I can't imagine how we all would have felt if he had hurt himself or someone else while driving with his advancing Alzheimer's disease. My dad went through a period of denial, telling others that the DMV was unfair and that he did not have Alzheimer's. My mom was the other loser here. She now had the added role of being his full-time chauffeur.

Navigating the health and social service system is hard enough when you're an educated person working in the health field. That task becomes so much harder for foreign-born or immigrant families. Not knowing the language and system can severely suppress their earning potential. This was the case for my family in earlier years, and it was their lack of financial resources that strained their lives and made everything that much more difficult.

During my time as a Health and Aging Policy Fellow in our nation's capital, I was always astounded to hear some of my White colleagues question why minorities were so opposed to nursing homes or retirement communities. After all, their loved ones were in a fantastic facility. Not only did they assert that their family member's health perked up after moving to one of these facilities, but they also had made new friends, had fine dining, and were being escorted all about town for many engaging recreational activities, and so on and so forth. Yes, and I bet that cost at least $100,000 per year, almost twice the median income of many families. For most, this option of expensive nursing homes and retirement communities is unthinkable, not just because of the prohibitive cost but because of the cultural judgment that would ensue. Putting your family member into a facility would deem you as an unworthy outcast who neglected to uphold their filial duties. Let me be clear, though. I do not oppose assisted living care.

In fact, we are exploring this option for my father, should he need it as his Alzheimer's worsens and my mother's already delicate health takes a turn for the worse. In *Chapter 7: Housing and Living*, we dive deeper into affordable housing concerns and options for minority families.

Not having enough money makes it hard to hire the right people to make home visits or get care of any kind. When you're working full shifts at work, the idea of taking two hours off to take a parent to the doctor comes with the fear of putting your job at risk. Witnessing these struggles firsthand as a first-generation "immigrant," I knew I had to make a difference. Money buys medications, medical supplies, and that Uber rides to the doctor's appointment. With these lessons in mind, I knew early on I had to learn more about the world of money. In this book, you'll notice that I focus on helping caregivers understand their own history and relationship with their own money and the financial demands of caregiving to avoid the common pitfalls.

Caring in the Community

Caregiving is challenging because you are trying to help a medically compromised person, often with multiple underlying health conditions, who may struggle with the psychological impact of their situation and doing so with little to no help. Frequently, paid caregivers can cost a considerable amount of money compared to the earning potential of some families. Family caregivers end up taking on this role and do the work of a paid caregiver while trying to juggle the day-to-day responsibilities of their own family life. The process becomes even more daunting with age and the related declines in physical and mental health.

Things are changing culturally in Mexican-American families, just like they are in many cultures, whether you're from the Philippines, India, Jamaica, or other parts of the world. Back in their home country of Mexico, my elder relatives may have been supported by their neighbors and community. But in the U.S., in 2021, with a more individualistic society (instead of collectivist cultures), adult children are living further and further away from their relatives, often relocating to find the best job prospects where they stand a better chance of becoming homeowners. Sometimes, Mexican-American elderly turn to each other for friendship and a sense of belonging. In 2009, I led focus groups at Kimball Senior Center in National City with large groups of primarily Mexican-American seniors. It was quite common to hear them refer to each other as family; one woman even saying that the only time she saw her daughter who lived across town was at church. She had to make up excuses to see her daughter and her grandchildren. Others talked about having close relatives currently living in Nebraska or Chicago—it was simply too expensive and far to travel to them often, especially in cold weather. And so their community friends became family.

Growing geographic distance and greater individualism are partly responsible for long-distance caregiving emerging as the norm amongst Mexican-American and other minority families. The concepts of taking care of the family are slowly being replaced by the drive towards individual work obligations and less towards the care of elders.

This acculturation process, where the minority and majority cultures blend, doesn't happen seamlessly (Crist et al., 2009). We often weave in and out of one predominant frame of mind. Behaviors and attitudes blend to form a new hybrid culture. Acculturation can be measured through language familiarity and usage, ethnic interaction, ethnic pride, and identity, cultural heritage, and generational proximity.

With Mexican and Hispanic caregivers, this *acculturation* process increases their sense of *familism* (putting the family's well-being over one's own interests). It reduces the individualistic effects of the U.S. culture (Crist et al., 2009). This association of acculturation and familism can be explained because, as immigrants are exposed to the dominant culture, they begin to value their family even more to maintain their sense of connection to their original culture and family connections. Other characteristics of familism are familial support, interconnectedness, honor, and subjugation of self for the family.

When I started this career path, some of my earliest jobs included working as a community outreach worker and health educator in San Diego. I would visit the community health centers and help migrant workers learn more about HIV/AIDS transmission, prevention, and healthy behaviors. Some of the migrant workers I visited through the community clinics included workers who lived in terrible conditions while caring for the racehorses seen at the Del Mar Fair. I've never enjoyed the San Diego County Fair (its new name) in the same way after what I saw in those days. Witnessing the migrant workers' living conditions left an impression on me during this formative time of my career. The horses seem to have better accommodations.

As an undergraduate research assistant at the University of California, San Diego (UCSD), I had the fun job of visiting families in the Logan Heights neighborhood, near the famous Chicano Park, to educate them about their food choices and physical activity. Sometimes the families invited me for dinner, and one family always had their daughter sing to me–she was an aspiring Mariachi singer. These interactions planted the seed for my work in public health. It's funny because at the time and even during part of my college career, I didn't know that public health was a 'thing.' You could pursue a career in public health and get a master's degree! It wasn't until another undergraduate student at the University of California, San Diego, introduced me to the field that I found my clear path ahead. Years later, our paths crossed again, and I learned that Dr. Hector Rodriguez had become a distinguished professor at UC Berkeley.

Then, as I progressed in college and pursued my master's and Doctorate in Public Health (DrPH), I continued my work with the migrant Mexican population, expanding my research into studying health inequities. I could perform field interviews and work with large datasets and help lead and write many research articles to analyze the experiences of older Mexican-Americans and their caregivers, as well as the effects of diabetes and other diseases in this minority group. Interviewing minority and immigrant families to learn about the challenges they faced for my research made me understand the daily struggles to survive in the face of meager resources. I could also see the resilience these caregivers had in the care of their aging relatives. What was even more important than learning about the effects of diseases on this population was learning about their attitudes and knowledge base regarding health conditions and preventive care. Much of it is driven by our immediate environment - where we live, work, and play.

The combination of my own family experiences with caregiving, a lifetime of research, work in the public health field, plus gerontology, has prompted me to write a book and share my knowledge and experience over the last two decades. Hopefully, this will help current caregivers and elders' journey through the aging process more smoothly. I aim to inspire a new generation of public health advocates and gerontologists to take care of the next generation of seniors.

Chapter 2

A Woman's Job

Cultural expectations in the Hispanic community, like many non-Western cultures, drive many of the decisions of both men and women. This is the reason for the disproportionate reliance on women to take on the role of caregivers. Upwards of 75% of all caregivers are female, and many women spend as much as 50% more time providing care than males (Institute on Aging).

Hispanic women take on 75% of caregiving in their families. In the Mexican population of the U.S., the average age of Hispanic caregivers is 42.7%–the lowest of all racial/ethnic groups (National Alliance for Caregiving and AARP, 2020). I saw these percentages play out in real life, as I spoke to many of the women who took on the primary role of caregiving. Part of this calling is rooted in cultural expectations of *marianismo* in Hispanic families, as well as the assumptions that women are seen as having the nurturing traits that make them better caregivers.

The Hispanic community's culture of *marianismo* has relegated women to these roles with or without their consent. You've already read about my mom's sequential roles as a caregiver to her sister-in-law and mother-in-law, as one example of the gender divide. One of my aunts (my biological uncle's wife) also often came to my paternal grandmother's house to bathe her mother-in-law. My aunts on my mother's side have also made some incredible feats in caring for my maternal grandmother, who celebrated her ninetieth birthday in 2020. My grandmother has shared her own caregiving stories with me about taking care of my great-grandmother and her oldest brother (Tío Juan), traveling miles regularly between San Diego and Rosarito, Mexico, to check in on them. These incredible women have set a high bar for what is to be expected. And an example of how to love and take care of family members–even as you are aging yourself. But times have changed, and we need to reexamine what it means to uphold these roles today.

Marianismo: Cultural Obligations of the Mexican Woman

Outside of Mexican culture, many people have heard of the word *machismo.* It is a term describing men where they are expected to be 'manly,' self-reliant, and able to take care of their family. Mexican men are expected to show aggressively their male characteristics and display their "macho" nature and come through for their family. This label, unfortunately, has hindered men's ability to find coping mechanisms and outlets for emotional support and may explain why 1 in 10 Mexican-American men grapple with alcoholism, including my dad.

On the other end of the spectrum, women in Mexican culture have perpetuated the ideas of *marianismo*. *Marianismo* is less well-known but still has a significant impact on Mexican culture today, making it harder for women to escape outdated views about women's roles. Many non-Western cultures have deeply entrenched ideas around filial piety that focus on women as the bearers of this torch. They may have other names for this.

Under *marianismo*, Mexican women are expected to display their feminine qualities, stay pure, and have moral strength. They are expected to identify strongly with and be attached to their nuclear and extended families, which includes an expectation that they will be the family caregivers. This dedication to their families because of *marianismo* can help explain why 61% of Latino caregivers are women; and that number is even higher for African-American caregivers at 66% and slightly lower for Asian Americans (58%). Other minority groups (besides Latino, African American, and Asian) are less studied and more often excluded from these studies, so it is difficult to gauge the extent of caregiving at home in other communities of color and immigrant populations (AARP, 2020).

Mexican *marianismo* was on full display in my household growing up–a predominance of females acting as caregivers to their nuclear and extended families. This explains why my mom took care of my dad's relatives and why my grandmother took care of her mom with such dedication. And here I am, a Mexican-American woman devoting her life's work to the caregiving field. I continue to carry on my family and cultural conditions, having worked with immigrant and minority communities early on and eventually choosing a path in public health and gerontology.

The Predominant Female Caregiver

Women overall add up to 75% of all caregivers and take on most caregiving duties (Institute on Aging). These caregivers (and their male counterparts) perform various tasks based on the individual's care needs. According to the Gallup-Healthways Well Being Index (Mendes, 2011), on average, thirteen days are used by caregivers each month for activities such as shopping, food prep, housekeeping, laundry, transportation, and medications. Six days per month are used for feeding, dressing, grooming, walking, bathing, and help toileting. Thirteen hours per month are used for researching care services and diseases, appointments, and organizing finances.

Women don't just make up most caregivers; they also work the most hours per week. In 2016, they worked up to 50% more than men on caregiving duties since 2009 (21.9 hours per week for women vs. 17.4 for men in 2009). Male caregivers were less likely to provide personal care and would rather pay someone to help with these types of tasks. Women not only work more hours, but they also perform more difficult and physically demanding jobs. About one-third (36%) of female caregivers provide the most arduous tasks versus 24% for males (males are more likely to help with less onerous tasks like finances and scheduling care) (National Alliance for Caregiving and AARP, 2009).

Performing these hard tasks, at an average age of fifty years old (and forty-three years old for Latinos), for an extended period, will put a strain on the caregiver's body. Older caregivers, sixty-five and over, make up 34% of all caregivers. Imagine helping someone take a bath and then helping them back to their bed or chair. Now imagine doing this for at least four years–which is the average duration a person will be in the role of caregiver (National Alliance for Caregiving and AARP, 2015). Maybe this is you?

About 39% of all caregivers are caregiving for at least five years with 15% working for over ten years. This type of physically demanding work will put a strain on anyone– especially an older caregiver beginning to face health issues of their own.

Let me share an example here for a moment. There is no 'day off' for my mom when caring for my dad, whose Alzheimer's has only deteriorated further in recent years. She must find a workaround, regardless of her physical limitations. Her shoulder pain has become unbearable, and she has had to go about her caregiving duties with an aching, stiff shoulder. Over the holidays, I noticed how she cleverly avoided straining her arm while she cleaned up bathroom 'accidents' with one arm, juggling the spray bottle under her chin and rag under her foot, trying her darndest to bend down carefully. One can make these workarounds for only so long before a caregiver's health takes a toll.

The data validates the reliance on the female caregiver that I observed in my family. My dad was the only male who was engaged in caregiving to his aging parents. Many of my dad's male siblings did not see their parents for months or years at a time, let alone actively take part in eldercare. My purpose in describing the imbalance of responsibility on women here is not to aggravate anyone but to acknowledge this reality. The country, however, is beginning to turn the tide. There have been more discussions than ever among policymakers in recent years on reforming family medical leave at the federal level. This would enable caregivers, often women, to take time off as needed to handle these responsibilities without quitting their job or reducing their hours.

For now, the best recourse for full-time employees is the

Family and Medical Leave Act (FMLA), which is better known for permitting employees to have twelve weeks of unpaid time off for the birth of a child (U.S. Department of Labor). However, lesser known is that FMLA entitles employees to take those twelve weeks of paid time off to care for their spouse, child, or parent with a serious health condition (U.S. Wage and Hour Division, 2015). FMLA defines 'parent' as the biological, adoptive, step, or foster parent of an employee or an individual. The term 'parent' does not include the employee's parents-in-law. Unfortunately, FMLA does little for most caregivers whose loved one needs ongoing care beyond twelve weeks. Let's face it, even a week or two without wages can deal a severe blow to most people's budgets.

The Caregiver's Gift: What They Give to Their Loved Ones

Working so many hours and in such a physically demanding role, caregivers put their own health aside as they tend to the needs of their sick family members and their own family. Latina caregivers, in all age groups, are less likely to receive regular preventive care than the non-caregiving population and are shown to engage less often in any form of physical activity (Paz and Massey, 2016). It's a twisted irony that those who take care of the sick can end up in worse shape, becoming physically, mentally, and financially 'sick.'

Formal, paid caregivers, those who form part of the direct care workforce, often leave the field because of disability, bad backs and do so at higher rates than women in other career roles (Baughman and Smith, 2012). I have met many women of color who are caretakers to seniors in their day job, only to go home and do it all over again for their own aging or disabled loved ones. It's no surprise, given that 59% of direct care workers are people of color (PHI, 2021). Direct care workers who are paid for caring for seniors or persons with a disability deliver services primarily in the home. They tend to cobble together multiple part-time caregiving jobs, often have no health insurance, and live in households at the poverty level. Non-White and Hispanic/Latinos make up 17% of this workforce (Montgomery, Holley, Deichert, and Kosloski, 2005).

Part of my work in this field has been educating women on what it takes to turn those skills into paid work. We currently provide a free guide on Kapok's website: Becoming a Paid Caregiver *https://www.multiculturalcaregiving.net/becoming-a-paid-caregiver-a-kapok-guide-2/)* and in Spanish, Como Ser un Cuidador Remunerado: *(https://www.multiculturalcaregiving.net/como-ser-un-cuidador-remunerado-kapok-guia/).*

What I witnessed with my family rings true with many direct care workers and caregivers. A study found that most direct care workers work less than full-time, have no health coverage (Montgomery, Holley, Deichert and Kosloski, 2005), and live in households below 200% of the Federal Poverty Level. Besides the reduced working hours, one in four nursing home workers and one in three aides lacked health coverage. Lacking health insurance puts their health at risk in case of an emergency and can cause a financial disaster. Luckily, advocates such as PHI (*https://phinational.org*) work around the clock on significant research and policy changes to improve these conditions for direct care workers.

It's not only these short-term sacrifices caregivers make for their families and patients, but also in the long-term, these caregivers also sacrifice the development of skills that help ensure their expertise and experiences will be in demand in the marketplace. And, with such physically demanding work, it will be hard for them to maintain the same level of strength as they get older. I've seen many women in their fifties and sixties who were once caregivers to young children ask for help looking for childcare work with either newborns or children over five and older who didn't expect to be carried all the time. Another young gal in her sixties quit her job at the grocery store because her arthritic hands had trouble gripping produce all day long. Their aching bodies just couldn't take it anymore. Leaving their own health conditions untreated will also spell disaster for long-term employment and financial prospects (Baughman and Smith, 2012).

Another issue is that working low-wage and part-time jobs can lead to the lack of retirement plan benefits. Many factors can contribute to being ready for retirement. High rates of part-time work (unless the employee contributes to their own retirement plan) can make it less likely for the employee to receive employer-sponsored 401k plans. One study found that besides working reduced hours, other factors, such as wages, age, sex, income, employer size, and employment type (public vs. private), all contribute to how ready Hispanics/Latinos are for retirement (Brown & Oakley, 2018). These factors that contribute to retirement readiness make sense—to save for retirement benefits, you need the disposable income that you can save. But if you are working part-time and in a low-wage job, setting aside funds can feel like a pipe dream. Plus, income is generally lower for those working in the public sector.

For Hispanics/Latinos specifically aged fifty-five to fifty-nine, over half do not have any accumulated assets (in any type of retirement account) (Orszag and Rodriquez, 2005). Only 50% have a basic transactional bank account (checking or savings account)! That came as no surprise to me. When my parents took over the day-to-day finances and medical care for my grandmother, they had to start from scratch. She used to keep her Social Security funds rolled up tightly like cigarettes stashed throughout her house. You can't blame her for not trusting those around her. It's been well established that most abuse against seniors is perpetrated by someone close to them, usually a family member or caregiver. Even when Hispanics/Latinos have a retirement account, they have one-third fewer savings than White people (Brown and Oakley, 2018).

Chapter 3

Breaking Traditions During Times of Change

I always knew, especially when witnessing the caregiving and eldercare in my family, that a disproportionate share of the sacrifices was borne by the women in the family. Feminine traits such as being warm, sensitive, and deferential are often viewed as essential to help build relationships with elders and put seniors at ease during challenging health events. That's just some of what women hear when the caregiving tasks are thrust upon them.

Women, hands down, have always shouldered the greater burden of eldercare in many non-Western cultures. Don't get me wrong though, there are exceptions. I know of several men who have contributed to the care of their parents, including my dad and even younger men like my brother-in-law, Carlos. Their caretaking roles took on a different form, however. They assisted with light-duty things, such as shopping for their groceries or taking them to the doctor. The heavy-duty work was more often left for the women in the family, including daughters-in-law. My mother-in-law has shared she even washed her mother-in-law's laundry from the nursing home regularly up until she passed away.

The women in my family seemed to follow cultural norms around eldercare, down the traditional path, where they often became primary caregivers. But with the younger generation today, changes in demographics and attitudes are upending the landscape of eldercare. Families live further away from each other, and younger generations are more open to seeking outside help to care for aging relatives.

Caregivers can seek support through many social programs to get help with aging family members and elders. Contrary to popular belief, the only form of help outside the home is not nursing homes or other forms of institutionalized care. Many new programs help caregivers to care for aging relatives right at home. Research on the potential savings and personal preference has finally caught up with policy, and more health insurers are willing to cover some degree of home health care. States' Medicaid programs are supporting more programs that help with transitional care than ever in the past. It's true that requirements are often strict and wait-lists are growing. At least there is growing acceptance that it's not only cheaper to keep people at home but often better for their quality of life and well-being.

Changing Attitudes and Cultural Shifts

In my family, the first immigrants from Mexico brought with them the collectivist culture and traditional gender roles. Not that they were socialists, but they believed in working

28

for the greater good of the family unit. It was obvious they believed in the traditional values instilled in them by the elders in the family. While *machismo* and *marianismo* have their pros and cons, one thing is certain—they both infuse values of dedication and an unspoken obligation to look out for the family. The men, with their *machismo*, provided for and protected their families. The men in my family took on the manly jobs in construction or took on jobs in the service industry. Meanwhile, with their *marianismo*, the women were dedicated to taking care of the home and all family members, with some exceptions. The concept of familism (the tradition of putting family before individual needs) is a significant factor in this dedication to caring for aging relatives (Gaugler et al., 2006; Herrera et al., 2008; Nguyen et al., 2003; Sabogal et al., 1987).

Where previously one could not fathom the idea of sending a grandparent to a nursing facility, the rate of institutionalized care has steadily risen among Mexican families. Frankly, even the most seasoned caregiver cannot handle the care of a loved one with severe conditions, such as advanced Alzheimer's or someone who recently had a stroke and has since become paralyzed. Previously, it was almost unheard of for elders in Mexican communities to be placed in nursing homes because of the cultural norms of *marianismo* and familism. Doing so showed the inconvenience placed upon the family unit by an aging relative. A sense of shame loomed over you, having neglected your duties as a caregiver and shrugging off your responsibilities to your parents. Often, placing family members in nursing homes was something only 'Americanos' did for their family members; it was a symptom of our being raised in an individualist society. I'm here to tell you to end the guilt and know that you're doing your best!

You wouldn't be reading this book if you weren't doing your best to navigate these waters. Evidence shows that minority representation in assisted living facilities, nursing homes, and respite care programs is increasing exponentially. You're not alone. The reasons behind this trend is far more complicated than more minority/immigrant adult children shedding culturally rooted pressures. This new generation is focused on making money and advancing their careers instead of staying home and taking care of their family. Who can blame us? The economy has been unforgiving to our current generation, meaning we must work harder and longer just to make ends meet. Student loan debt also hangs over us like a dark cloud. My own student loan debt rivals our mortgage. So, thank you for buying this book. Besides being the sandwich generation, this new generation is working outside of the home and having to find work where they can get it. To a certain extent, it comes down to weighing out the opportunity costs–the cost to the family member to take care of their elders versus going out into the job market and pursuing a career (Brown, Herrera, and Angel, 2013).

This opportunity cost is becoming more and more critical as the standard of living is decreasing in the U.S. because of an increase in living costs. More is at stake as the income inequality between the middle class and higher-income households grows. On his income of $8 - $12/hour, my dad was able to raise a family of five in the 80's and 90's. Having anything besides rice and beans for dinner was a luxury, and eating out happened on rare occasions, but we managed. We knew it was a good day if we were treated for dinner at our favorite joint, La Bella Pizza, in downtown Chula Vista. We celebrated my daughter's fourth birthday at La Bella Pizza not too long ago, primarily for nostalgic reasons. Back then, my dad's salary was all we had to work with, and luckily my mom knew how to stretch a dollar. Today, that wage would not be enough to survive on, let alone make you a homeowner. You would be hard-pressed today to be a homeowner on this wage, with median home prices up approximately 400% since the early 1980s.

Inflation is adding to this income inequality because as the purchasing power of the dollar decreases, food, housing, and general living expenses are increasing faster than real wages are growing. Add in rising asset prices, and you have a situation where *the rich get richer, and the poor get poorer.* An example of the rich getting richer is the wealth gap more than doubling between the richest and poorest families between 1989 and 2016 (Schaeffer, 2020). For workers on the lower end of this economic scale, wages have declined since 1973, and the number of middle-class jobs has been declining due to offshoring and globalization. The U.S. has the highest inequality rating among the Group of Seven (G7) countries (Canada, France, Germany, Italy, Japan, United Kingdom, and the United States) (Schaeffer, 2020).

Keeping an aging person at home while working is a definite possibility. However, maybe we are missing how challenging this situation can be, not just for Hispanics but also for all minority communities. I witnessed firsthand the challenges and financial sacrifices made to keep your loved ones in the home. Working outside the home may not just be a cultural wave of Hispanics/Latinos denouncing traditional expectations of care. Instead, it is fast becoming a necessity for many families.

Research studies show that older adults across most racial or ethnic groups claim that they do not want to be a burden on their children while stating that they prefer to 'age in place,' which means to age at home. Aging in place has almost become a mantra for advocates seeking a wider range of services for seniors to help them live independently. Americans take pride in going at it alone. But assuming that living independently is the end goal can be counterproductive. Some experts, including myself, believe that 'aging in place' isn't necessarily a good thing for everyone. Some older adults' quality of life is best served by living with family or in a retirement community where they can be monitored by trained medical staff and benefit from new friends and recreational activities. It's essential to work with your loved one's providers and talk with the family to determine when and if your aging relative reaches a point where living alone or at home no longer serves them well.

Let's take my mother, Marisela, for example. A stubborn, outspoken woman. In Mexico, she was a teacher. Once we moved to the U.S., my mom was a homemaker. She raised three daughters and built an incredible home and garden in San Diego. I remember the first time I took my daughter to daycare: my mom let me know she didn't understand why women have kids only to pawn them off on other people. Just what I needed to hear, right? She tells us she will live and die at her current address and doesn't want to be a burden on any of us. We'd be damned for attempting to move her in her advanced years. My mom has the benefit of her dedicated and capable adult daughters, so she'll have little to worry about, but this is not the case for many families out there.

Yet, for the past two years, she's developed troubling issues with her shoulder and knees. Because of COVID-19, her rotator cuff and knee surgery had to be postponed to 2021. Right now, she's caregiving for my father with one arm and grabs her granddaughter with one arm. What will this look like ten years from now? Keep in mind that Latinos have very high longevity. My great-grandmother lived to 105, and my grandparents that have passed did so in their mid-nineties. My maternal grandmother recently celebrated her ninety first birthday. Even my father, at eighty-three, has surpassed the upper end of the age range on the longevity scale as to how long people with Alzheimer's survive from their date of diagnosis. So out goes that scientific research.

My mother has been caring for my father for two decades, who is in the last stages of Alzheimer's, based on my educated assessment. Imagine how frustrating it can be to help an elder who may be uncooperative at times because of Alzheimer's disease. Not to mention the emotional distress of seeing a loved one struggle to speak or recognize his own granddaughter. At some point, any caregiver may reach their breaking point and want to throw in the towel.

Is Institutional Care So Bad?

As bad as it may sound, institutionalizing an elder in a nursing home has its benefits. One advantage of a nursing home is access to the specialized caregiving training employees receive. The nursing home staff have the educational background and licensing requirements to become professional caregivers and can provide skilled care in a managed facility. Another advantage is the social aspect of having companions in a nursing facility, assuming your loved one can still engage in meaningful conversations with others. In Chapter 7: Housing and Living, we discuss some challenges and solutions for finding an affordable place that provides adequate care. Your family member can find other seniors or staff of similar cultures with who they can engage with in their primary language or relate to on a more personal level.

Caregivers may have work responsibilities or childcare demands, leaving the elder at home with no modes of transportation. I've come across families where every adult worked shifts that created a void on the home front. There was literally no one at home with the elder relative for ten hours straight. Senior parents may also find it difficult to be under their adult child's authority or feel restricted, trapped, or unhappy. They may feel helpless to speak up. I had an elderly Honduran couple in Maryland reach out to me once, begging to help them find a way to move out of their daughter's house. In their words, "we feel like prisoners."

Transportation has been reported to be one of older adults' greatest concerns. Outside of finances and socialization, a lack of mobility is a big predictor of a seniors' quality of life. Transportation gives an elder their independence and allows them to be more social. Lack of transportation can lead to social isolation if a senior is stuck at home all day. Whether it is taking part in reunions with friends or family, running errands, or going to church, transportation is an essential means of keeping seniors in touch with the world out there. It's no surprise to hear that COVID-19-related lockdowns were detrimental to seniors' mental health. Not all seniors are as adept at FaceTime as my five-year-old is today or have the means and tech savvy to use Instacart to order groceries.

Regardless of whether a nursing home or another skilled nursing facility is used, no one can presumably be more caring and patient than one's own family when they are fully present. However, a family member who is overwhelmed by life's demands may not be able to provide the level of care a loved one needs and even unintentionally neglect them or put their life at risk. These are important considerations for anyone contemplating a significant change to their loved one's living arrangements.

Demographic Shifts

Now let's talk about how women in the workforce and the number of children will influence their options to age or need long-term care. Research shows that the fewer kids an older adult have, especially living nearby, the greater their likelihood of being in a nursing home (NVSS, 2018). More women are entering the job market than ever before, reducing the number of caretakers available to care for aging relatives at home (Reinhard et al., 2011).

The U.S. has now hit a forty-year low in its fertility rate. This means that women are having fewer children. Fertility rates have fallen for young women in their thirties, especially amongst minority groups (Stone, 2018). With the natural shift in cultural norms in the first generation of immigrant children, demographics are also shifting for Mexican-American families. Latinos, having one of the historically higher fertility rates, are among the minority groups that have seen the largest decline.

Fertility rates fell 5.9% overall for Mexican immigrants from 2008 to 2009 in the U.S. (Livingston, 2011). The drop in fertility rates has resulted in fewer children (2.9 births less per one thousand women) for women aged fifteen to forty-four years. This trend can be devastating because women make up 74% of the Hispanic caregivers (Evercare and National Alliance for Caregiving, 2008). This suggests that many more Hispanics will depend upon institutionalized care and formal, or paid, support for their aging care needs over the coming years. This is also bad news for the general population, mainly because Hispanics and other people of color tend to enter the direct care workforce at much higher rates than other populations.

The reduction in fertility rates results in a smaller pool of relatives to care for the elders in their family (Fennell et al., 2010). Caregiving may have been shared by multiple women or family members, as more of them are pulled into the workforce, caregiving tasks may end up falling upon one individual in the family, compounding the emotional and financial stress on that person. Besides this, more stress and a reduction in time available have helped push institutionalization to higher rates (Fennell et al., 2010). In short, we could be headed for a time when seniors are unable to find adequate help, paid or unpaid.

Sandwiched Between Two Generations

The 'Sandwich Generation' refers to people who are in their thirties, forties, and fifties and provide support, financial or otherwise, for both their aging parents and children at the same point in time. The children of the current sandwich generation have had it especially tough since the Great Recession. Many have moved back home even after completing a college degree, prolonging the time these parents help multiple generations.

Life can be stressful for these caregivers because they are taking care of the needs of three generations of family members while trying to live their own lives. They also provide emotional support. Throw in a spouse and grandchildren, and you can imagine what a stressful time this can be.

Caregiver burnout is a genuine phenomenon caused when the caregiver foregoes their own self-care to take care of their familial responsibilities. The lack of time for relationships, hobbies, and downtime may cause various psychological issues. Depression, chronic health problems, and fatigue are common problems. Having to drop out of the workforce or reduce hours can also lead to financial hardship, further compounding the stress and burnout.

How Far Away?

Distance is another factor that may play into a caregiver's burnout and how they provide care to elders. Most caregivers live within an hour's drive of aging parents or elder they care for. Further broken down: 75% of caregivers live within twenty minutes, 13% of caregivers live twenty minutes to one hour away, and long-distance caregivers live up to seven hours' travel (an average of 450 miles) (National Alliance for Caregiving and AARP, 2015).

Living in Chandler, Arizona, I'm now a good five-and-a-half-hour drive to my parents. Compare that to early 2019, where we had to make a five-hour flight from Virginia to San Diego. It was an enormous hassle. I had to arrange for a cat sitter and take several days off work. Now, we can make it a weekend visit. Not everyone has personal time off or sick days to use for those occasions. With my daughter now in school-age, I'm also not okay with her skipping class unless there's an emergency. In my household, school and homework is priority *Numero Uno*.

Dedicated long-distance caregivers also have the highest annual expenses related to caregiving, outspending those who live with their care recipients and those who care for a nearby family member (Reinhard, Friss, Houser, Choula, & Evans, 2019). These long-distance caregivers are younger than caregivers living in close proximity to the elder needing care. There are a few reasons for this. The younger age of the caregiver correlates with a younger parent that may still be in the earlier stages of an illness. This is also a reflection of changing times, with more caregivers having to manage care from a distance to keep their job and home life. Lastly, they may be the only child, and have no choice in the matter.

As the elder's physical health deteriorates, they may need more around-the-clock help. My two aunts, Sara and Sylvia, on my mother's side, for example, lived with their parents, including during the time my step-grandfather became ill before passing. He was a brilliant and giving man with a slight temper. They now team up to care for my grandmother. She continues to live with them, making caregiving convenient by allowing them to pursue their careers while managing my grandmother's care at their fingertips. As my grandmother has experienced more trips to the hospital in the past year, their stress levels have certainly increased. Both aunts are devout Catholics who turn to their faith often for solace and emotional strength. Every situation will be unique, and in the end, you and your family will arrive at a plan that suits your situation best.

My in-laws recently moved from Maryland and into a nearby town this year. They say they were motivated to move to watch their granddaughter grow up. Besides their company, my husband and I know that their move here is a convenient arrangement for us. My husband seems totally oblivious to their needs and often needs a kick to check up on them. Their proximity will make those needs more visible. On the plus side, my husband won't have to travel across the country to check in on his parents as they age. That would mean expensive round-trip flights, taking days off work and lost wages, plus playing single parent for a week while he's gone. For us, that's a big deal, especially as we are caring for an active five-year-old kid with type 1 diabetes who has an intensive routine.

Ditching the Guilt–Getting Help

Caregivers, especially newer ones, must learn to navigate the system and learn about the resources and options of eldercare at their disposal. Minorities and immigrant families, being new to the country, rarely know the system and are wary of all required of being considered for any program. Add a language barrier and limited financial resources on top of this and looking for and receiving help can be a challenge. In this chapter, I cover the most essential social programs as well as entitlements, such as Medicare and Social Security.

Luckily, in the U.S., there are social programs to help those in times of need. Where would we be as a society if we didn't provide this safety net? No one ever thinks they'll need a hand, until they do. The exorbitant cost of healthcare and housing today, along with failures to pay decent livable wages, have made it difficult for even full-time working families to afford the cost of aging care.

Before we dive into the specifics of each program, head over to the National Council on Aging's (NCOA) website and see what benefits the senior is eligible for receiving. I worked at NCOA for many years and can personally vouch for the amount of scrutiny that my colleagues put into researching and compiling these resources. You start by completing the online assessment, and the system populates a list of programs that you may qualify for to help with medical, housing, food, transportation, and more. Eligibility information, application materials and other information is provided, where available. The survey can be accessed at *https://www.benefitscheckup.org.*

Another excellent place to start with finding any service for the aging is with your local AAA. No, not that AAA. I'm referring to your Area Agency on Aging. They will have insight into caregiver programs in your area and the requirements involved. They may go by different names in each region. You can find a listing by visiting the National Association of Area Agencies on Aging *(https://www.n4a.org)*.

One very popular program in the U.S. is called Medicaid. Each state has its own Medicaid program designed to provide social services to help people who meet specific financial criteria. Medicaid is helpful to new immigrants as it provides them health coverage. Then, once they are established financially, they can move off Medicaid and purchase health insurance from their state's health exchange or work-based insurance.

Social Security is a well-known social program for the elderly. It was created in 1935 by President Roosevelt under the Social Security Act. This program was designed to pay retired workers aged sixty-five and older an income after their retirement. Legal workers pay into this system through payroll taxes over their working life and must meet the minimum requirements to take part in the system. Workers qualify by earning forty credits throughout their working life. Workers earn a credit (with a max of four credits per year) for each $1,410 in earnings, so it is relatively easy to qualify. However, the more one earns, and the longer one contributes to the system, the more they ultimately receive in retirement benefits.

The age at which the senior starts taking retirement benefits also affects the benefits received at retirement age. Some workers, for various reasons, choose to take Early Retirement at age sixty-two. Others decide to take retirement at Full Retirement Age (FRA) age sixty-five and receive more benefits. Still, others continue to work and take Late

Retirement at the age of seventy! Someone working until age seventy will receive more than someone who retires earlier. At age seventy, the benefits from Social Security for working additional years no longer exist, but the purpose gained from work does.

In 2020, the maximum retirement benefits for someone taking Early Retirement (age sixty-two) was $2,265 per month, Full Retirement Age (age sixty-five) was $3,011 per month, and Late Retirement (age seventy) was $3,790 per month. These numbers are subject to Social Security's cost of living adjustments (COLA) which increase benefits based on inflation rates in the government's consumer price index (CPI). Of course, all situations are unique. As seniors approach age sixty-two, it would be in their interest to make an appointment with a Social Security agent to review their qualifications and potentially apply to begin their retirement benefits. For a more in-depth look at Social Security benefits, in English and En Español, you can visit the Kapok website at: *https://www.multiculturalcaregiving.net/social-security-retirement-benefits* or *https://www.multiculturalcaregiving.net/todo-lo-que-usted-necesita-saber-sobre-sus-prestaciones-de-jubilacion-del-seguro-social/.*

Social Security also has other programs designed to help the disabled or blind: **Social Security Disability Insurance (SSDI)** and **Social Security Income (SSI).** Once qualifications are met for SSDI, the disabled person may receive Medicare Part A, B, and D regardless of the person's age. SSI has similar qualifications as SSDI with some differences, as calculations are made with income and resources considered.

Medicare is another federal program designed to provide health insurance to Social Security retirees. Medicare comprises various parts. Part A, hospital insurance, is given to all Medicare recipients who qualify. Part A recipients must pay into Social Security and qualify for Medicare by earning at least a mandatory forty credits. Each credit is gained by working and earning at least $1,260, with a maximum of four credits earned per year. Part A covers inpatient care, skilled nursing facility care, hospice care, and home health care. You can sign up for Part A during the Initial Enrollment Period 3 months before, the month of, and three months after turning sixty-five.

Part B, medical insurance, must be purchased through an insurance broker during the General Enrollment Period (January 1–March 31). Part B covers doctors or health care providers, outpatient care, home health care, medical equipment, and various preventive services. Plan participants may also purchase another plan called Medicare Supplemental Insurance (or MediGap) to go along with their Part B health insurance. This add-on to their insurance policy pays for the 20% coinsurance amount, which drastically reduces out-of-pocket amounts.

Finally, there is the prescription plan called Part D, which is administered by private insurance companies, but must follow Medicare guidelines. Often, plans are offered at a $0 premium or very low cost. Whatever plan the seniors choose to sign up for, make sure you find a trusted insurance broker to do business with; different degrees in quality of service and ethics exist, especially in the financial services sector. For free and truly objective assistance on selecting the best Medicare plan for you or a loved one, connect with a counselor from your State's SHIP (State Health Insurance Assistance Programs) *https://www.shiphelp.org/*. SHIP is federally funded program and intended help seniors understand the complexities of Medicare and select the best plan without coercion. They do get booked up quickly around the enrollment period, which is typically mid-October to early December for basic Medicare. So be sure to schedule an appointment early.

Another program that can help with putting food on the table is the **Supplemental Nutrition Assistance Program (SNAP)**. This is a United States Department of Agriculture (USDA) program providing food security for low-income, elderly, and disabled people. Specific calculations are made to determine a person's financial eligibility. The program considers various factors, including age, disability, household size, gross monthly income, standard deductions, child support, shelter deduction, etc. SNAP may help supplement and offset some food costs of the elder and help relieve some financial strain from the caregiver.

Other social services programs are geared towards caregiving and even provide financial support to those taking care of elders or the disabled. Many of these are driven at the state or county level, so it's important to contact your local Area Agency on Aging to learn more about the application process and services. As an example, in Arizona, the Arizona Department of Economic Security (DES) manages the Family Caregiver Support program, which provides resources specifically for caregivers, such as training, counseling, support groups, respite care (to relieve caregivers temporarily), and other supplemental benefits. The DES and other similar state programs around the country, may even pay individuals for providing caregiving to their family members.

Did you know that every state will have a network for senior centers, many of which provide a free or low-cost lunch to seniors? Don't underestimate the quality of the food there either! I've eaten lunch at more senior centers that I can count through my work and meetings with seniors and caregivers. What's great about them is that the cooks will tailor the dishes to the center's patrons, so local ethnic cuisine is always on the menu. It's a great place to socialize too. I recall that my mom told me that my grandma had invited her out for a yummy lunch one day. She got ready and they headed out.

ANGELICA HERRERA VENSON, DRPH

My mom later told me that she didn't realize they were going to go grab lunch at the senior center, and she went on about how stuffed she was from the delicious meal.

In California, In-Home Supportive Services (IHSS), is a Medi-Cal program designed to help those over sixty-five years of age (disabled or blind included) remain in their homes. This social services program pays for caregivers to help with 'authorized tasks.' These tasks include housework, grocery shopping, meal prep, laundry, personal care services, and accompaniment to medical appointments. The great part of the IHSS program is the choice you have in who you select as your caregiver. This can be a contractor you hire or a family member or friend. With such a unique model, 70% of care providers in California under IHSS are family members. Hiring a family member or friend can cause more personalized and compassionate care. The wages, federally funded, are paid to the caregiver to provide financial incentives and help offset any wages lost in the caregiving activities.

Another useful social support system here in the U.S. is the various housing programs available (reviewed more in-depth later in the book). While these services are in high demand, they may be useful in acquiring subsidized or low-cost housing options. You can learn about the various local programs by visiting the local public housing authority or learning about the federal government Section 8 Housing Voucher Program and Section 202 housing programs. Your local department of health and housing may also help. Local, state, and even federal programs provide low-income housing and even supplement housing costs for eligible people.

As you can see, there are many social programs in the U.S. for healthcare, retirement, disability, food, and housing. The challenging part is to understand that these programs exist and be willing to get the ball rolling. Where demand is higher, it is not unusual to be put on waiting lists for any of these services. Be diligent and remain patient. Expect that there will be times that you feel like you're going in circles, hitting a wall, put on hold for eternity, disrespected, and feel completely confused. Stay the course. There is great demand and overworked case managers, and frontline staff are usually inundated with requests. Don't be afraid to ask for an interpreter or verify the status of an application. Don't assume anything. Your persistence will pay off, and these programs will help lessen the financial strain on caregivers and their elders.

Chapter 4

The Search for Caregiving Resources

With all the challenges facing caregivers, such as cultural expectations, demographic shifts, and financial obligations, you need to make sure that your parent or family member gets the attention they need. As a caregiver, you may feel like there is nowhere to look for help and resources. But what happens when the senior in your life has health conditions that worsen, and your family reaches the conclusion that it's time to get outside help? It may be time to look into adult day health centers, home respite care, assisted living facilities, or other services. However, there's one new challenge to contend with—finding the right program or person to help can be like finding a needle in a haystack. Culture and language come into play for many seniors and can make it harder to find high-quality healthcare suitable for your loved ones where they will feel comfortable and accepted.

For my Aunt Chelo, as an example, we had to research and visit several Adult Day Health Centers before finding one that had Spanish-speaking staff and other seniors. Initially, she was stuck in an Adult Day Health Center where one lovely Filipino staff member spoke a little Spanish. My aunt had learned a good amount of English as an adult. She worked in the U.S., but like many seniors who develop Alzheimer's, she reverted to her first language as her preference for communicating. The other problem that we also encountered is that some facilities that appeared to be culturally compatible were run down or in drug-ridden, high-crime neighborhoods.

Thankfully, there are still good support services and resources available to help minority caregivers and care recipients, even though such services may take a little more time and effort to find. In this chapter, we consider some barriers to finding high-quality care for seniors, tips and tools to find the right nursing home, and where to find community programs to support you in your caregiving efforts.

Barriers to Care

Hispanics face multiple barriers to receiving the care that will cater to their needs while also aligning with their values. Language is a major barrier, as nearly 75% of Hispanics speak Spanish at home, and 33% say they speak English less than "very well." Of the 50% who say that they have difficulty communicating with their healthcare provider, 44% face language barriers (9% report that the problem happens often). One study found that 50% of Hispanics above forty years of age have problems finding healthcare providers who speak Spanish, and 15% of the time, this is a frequent occurrence. The same study found that 67% of Hispanic seniors who speak a language other than English at home struggle to find Spanish-speaking healthcare staff to help with their healthcare (AP and NORC). Combine these poor English skills with a healthcare system with few Spanish-speaking healthcare professionals. The result is a cruel, slap-in-the-face healthcare experience for some Hispanic care recipients and their families. These challenges are made worse when a Hispanic individual has a low medical IQ and needs help to understand medical terms that may get misinterpreted during translation. Even with my years in healthcare, I still find myself in a daze, listening to my doctor rattle off a lot of nonsensical medical jargon. At the same time, they remain oblivious to their lack of clarity.

These language barriers often lead to stress, extra time, and effort, and increased travel time to receive medical care. Misunderstandings between patient and doctor or healthcare staff can lead to other unwelcome outcomes, such as delays in receiving care, higher healthcare costs, lower quality of care, and even receiving incorrect care (AP and NORC). It's safe to say that overcoming these language barriers may improve the quality of the healthcare experience. Yet, medical professionals are still astounded to see adults use their children as interpreters in the absence of other options. It's not ideal, but it's what we have. And which of you reading this book hasn't at one point done your best to interpret a colonoscopy procedure to their dad or A1c test results to a grandparent in their primary language?

Another notable barrier is a clear *cultural* disconnect between what Hispanics are used to and what healthcare professionals offer. With 39% of the Hispanic population born outside the U.S. and speaking a language other than English at home (AP and NORC), assimilating into the majority culture can be challenging. These immigrant seniors come to the U.S. with their own culture and religious beliefs already ingrained. Of the 50% of Hispanics above forty years of age who reported communication difficulties with their healthcare provider, 47% say this is because of cultural barriers (7% report the problem often occurs) (AP and NORC). Like other minority groups, Hispanics may also find it difficult to find providers who can understand their religious and spiritual practices. When my brother-in-law Carlos' father refused a blood transfusion before he passed, it took his family some time to explain his Jehovah's Witness preferences to providers.

There are other challenges, too, including not understanding the system and not knowing where to find all available public resources. When all these factors are combined, it's easy to see how healthcare becomes an incredibly challenging experience for minority groups. Later in this chapter, we will review more sources of help for caregivers and seniors to help maintain the elders' aging goals in place and maintain their independence.

Standards of Care Comparisons

During my time researching with minority communities, one thing became abundantly clear. You could never rely on those satisfaction surveys that many healthcare organizations conduct with their patients as a good representation on the quality of care provided. They are a terrible indicator of whether a patient is getting the treatment they need or being offered the same level of care as others. Foreign-born patients tend to skew these results by overrating their experience as five stars.

It's human nature to compare your level of service to anything you received before. There is often a stark contrast for many minorities who experienced an entirely different healthcare system in their home countries. Let's be frank.

Health services were altogether out-of-reach completely for some individuals without insurance in their home country. The cleanliness of the facilities and attention by providers in the U.S. compared to their home country may far exceed their expectations. It's no surprise then to find a disconnect between a minority patient's reported satisfaction and their actual care, especially when compared to the responses of their senior counterparts in the U.S.

An individual may have long wait times, may not be offered life-saving treatment, or be given the wrong prescription simply because of the color of their skin or the doctor's perception about their inability to pay for care. Yet, by the minority person's account, the experience was impressive enough to rate their services highly. This disconnect is seen most among foreign-born patients. Minorities who are foreign-born may believe the level of care they receive in the U.S. is phenomenal compared to their home country. While this may be true in some cases, minorities who come from a developing country with an inferior quality of care will have a distorted view. They may describe almost any care in the U.S. to be better than what they had in their home country, even if it is subpar in terms of American standards for quality nursing home and assisted living care.

This is a crucial context I want you to have as we begin discussing how to shop for residential or home health care options for your family members. Avoid getting taken in by first impressions. Expect and advocate for the best level of care, *equal* care, for your loved one.

Nursing Home Perceptions versus Reality

Research has shown that nursing homes serving minorities are often of lower quality, have fewer resources, and provide inferior care than those serving the majority population (Fennell et al., 2010, Mor et al., 2004, Smith et al., 2007). This only feeds existing fears that minorities have about placing a loved one in these types of facilities.

There are other misconceptions about nursing homes and assisted living facilities that make them an option of last resort. During one of my qualitative interviews with a Mexican-American caregiver, she described what she had heard about nursing home facilities. She said, "That's where seniors go to die," and that she'd heard that *"le hechan aguita"* to suggest that staff were actively dropping poison into residents' beverages. It sounds pretty crazy, but some immigrants have this mindset. In 2019, not far from here in Phoenix, Arizona, a young disabled Native American woman in a coma was raped while in the care of La Hacienda Long-term Care Facility (Geanous, 2019). This horrific event only further frightens many minority families and cement fears of potential neglect toward their loved ones. Combining this mindset with the cultural norms of *marianismo*, it is clear why so many immigrant families choose to tough it out and take care of loved one in the family home with little outside help.

While entry into nursing homes has been surging in previous years among minorities, this increase in use does not translate into confidence in the system (Feng et al., 2011, Herrera et al., 2013). One study found that only 16% of Hispanics aged forty and over were extremely or very confident that local nursing homes could meet their needs.

Similarly, only 18% were extremely or very confident that assisted living facilities could meet their needs. Less than 25% of Hispanics aged forty and older were confident that health aides (20%), assisted living communities (18%), and nursing homes (16%) could accommodate their cultural needs. 40% have little to no confidence in each of the three mentioned (AP and NORC).

The combination of incongruent long-term care services and financial factors has led to more care at home by family members. With such low confidence and expectations in certain parts of the healthcare system, what are minority elders' options for obtaining adequate healthcare services, especially services that cater to their language and cultural requirements?

Thankfully, it is still possible to find an excellent nursing home that meets elder's needs. There are many resources online that compile the information that you need and include useful ratings and feedback. However, it takes some research, planning, and consideration before you know the best type of long-term care facility for your situation and what your options are. The key to this part is to begin the process *before* you need a nursing home. Otherwise, when a crisis hits or an emergency requiring a nursing home arises, you may be forced to make a rushed decision that has adverse long-term consequences. Worst yet, the decision for post-rehabilitation or nursing home care will be made by the hospital's discharge nurse, not you. The last thing you want to do is have to move your loved one once they've begun settling into their residence. You'll definitely be getting an earful then.

Finding A Good Nursing Home

There are four major steps to looking for a nursing home:

Step 1: Finding Nursing Homes in Your Area

The first step involves asking people you trust for their recommendations. People to turn to can include family, friends, neighbors, and even coworkers. You could consider your doctor as well, as they will often have some patients in nursing homes and can make good recommendations for you. Begin by writing these recommendations down and starting a list of possible nursing home locations.

Then, start looking at a section on the Medicare website called **Care Compare** *(https://www.medicare.gov/care-compare/)*, which is an essential tool to have in your arsenal. It provides quality ratings and patient satisfaction scores that will surely help you narrow your list. You plug in your desired location (zip code or city), and the system will populate a list of nursing homes. You can conduct your search by provider type, including nursing homes, hospitals, home health agencies, rehabilitation centers, and more. I think I've used this tool at least three times in the past two months to help family and friends with narrowing their search for home health agencies.

You can also check on the Eldercare Locator website at *https://eldercare.acl.gov* to search for more long-term care planning resources. On the bottom of the Eldercare Locator website is a section called 'Helpful Resources,' where you can look for more 'Long Term Care Planning' resources. Another great resource is looking for your local **Aging and**

Disability Resource Centers (ADRCs). You can find out more about the ADRC and other aging-related resources on the **Administration for Community Living's (ACL)** website at *https://acl.gov/programs/connecting-people-services*. These resources are all good starting points to get a handle on your nursing homes and long-term care options.

Step 2: Compare the Quality of the Nursing Homes

This is done with the list of nursing homes you're considering from the previous step. Hopefully, the recommendations of nursing homes you get from your family, friends, or doctor will show up on the Care Compare website *(https://www.medicare.gov/care-compare/)*. That's always a good sign. The nursing homes on the Care Compare will have ratings based on various rankings using a 5-star system (a higher number of stars means a more favorable ranking). The four areas ranked are Overall Ranking, Health Inspections, Staffing, and Quality Measures.

◊ **Overall Ranking** is self-explanatory as it takes a global view of the business and gives it a ranking.

◊ **Health Inspections** is the score given to a nursing home from recent health inspections. This is a weighted score. While Medicare does not explicitly explain how it is weighted, my guess is that most recent health inspections are given more 'weight' in the score.

◊ **Staffing** is the third score given based on staffing hours of support staff such as registered nurses (RNs), licensed practice nurses (LPNs), licensed vocational nurses (LVNs), and nurse's aides. A higher score in this category means a better ratio between staff and nursing home residents.

◊ **Quality measures** are the final rating category and are based on various pieces of clinical data. This includes data such as residents with pressure ulcers or pressure injuries and the percentage of short-term residents who had an outpatient emergency visit. This appears to show how well taken care of the residents' health issues are.

◊ **Distance,** the last category, is actually not rated on Care Compare, but I insist you consider it. How far is the facility to your home? You'll want to make regular visits a part of your routine, so that staff stay alert that your loved one has an involved family member or advocate who will hold them accountable.

Another wonderful source of information is a long-term care *ombudsman.* The ombudsman's role is to advocate for the patients using long-term care and nursing home-type facilities. Like geriatric care managers, an ombudsman can be an excellent source of information regarding nursing homes. They are the individuals assigned by their state and local area agencies on aging to investigate customer complaints and suspected abuse in long-term care facilities.

You can also turn to the online Blue Pages, which are excellent sources of information regarding federal, state, and local offices. Information regarding the state's health department or state licensing agency websites is available in this resource. You will find information regarding the nursing home's responsibilities (or other skilled nursing facilities) and the most recent inspections of these facilities on the state's health department or licensing agency website. You may also use this resource to verify the facility's license.

Step 3: Visiting the Nursing Homes

When visiting the nursing home, you get to see the setting (instead of fancy marketing photos) and meet the staff. If you can't make it yourself, ask around your network and see if anyone you trust is willing to visit for you. Whether you or someone you trust visits, there are some general things to consider, including the nursing home's characteristics, such as the social, recreational, religious, and cultural activities. These are important because you want the resident to have the resources available to them so they can age well in all aspects of their life and access to what matters most to them. Other things to be on the lookout for are transportation to activities (especially to doctor visits), private spaces for visitors, therapy services available, and types of meals served. The question you may want to ask yourself continually is, "What will it be like to live here? Will I (or the elder) be taken care of well and treated with dignity?"

If no one is available to visit the facility for you, an alternate way to evaluate the nursing home is to call and speak to the staff on the phone. While you can't see the facility, you can ask many of the same questions in this information-gathering phase. After this call, it is still advisable to visit the nursing home in person when the opportunity presents itself. You don't want any regrets, and this is a serious decision that is difficult to undo.

It is advisable to call first and make an appointment

to see the nursing home for the initial visit. When you're preparing, you can print out a copy of the Medicare Nursing Home Checklist. This form can be changed to meet any elder's unique needs and requirements. You can download this form at: *https://www.medicare.gov/sites/default/files/2019-10/NursingHomeChecklist.pdf*

This Medicare checklist is divided into ten categories of things to look for when evaluating a nursing home. The categories are Basic Information, Safety, and Care, Preventing Abuse, Nursing Home Appearance, Nursing Home Living Spaces, Menus, and Food, Staff, Residents' Rooms, Activities, and Caring for Residents with Dementia. Within each major category on the Medicare checklist are common questions you may want to ask about or evaluate during your visit. Here, I've also integrated aspects of 'Cultural Fit' within each category.

The **Basic Information** category includes questions about Medicare or Medicaid certifications, availability of beds, specialized services, the proximity of nursing homes to family and friends, and details of the fees. This also boils down to whether there is space for your loved one in your desired time frame and whether you or your loved one can afford it.

The checklist's **Safety and Care** category include checking Medicare's nursing home ratings, nursing home arrangements with nearby hospitals, inspection reports showing quality of care issues, and correction of citations. Look at any news reports on the facility in Google News. Many poorly run facilities were exposed during the COVID-19 pandemic for lack of preparedness.

The **Preventing Abuse** category on the checklist includes evaluating the relationship between staff and residents, policies to report abuse or neglect, and nursing home citations for abuse-related issues.

The Nursing Home Appearance category on the checklist

has items such as grooming for residents, presence of pleasant or obnoxious odors, cleanliness, temperature, lighting, and noise levels. While appearance is helpful, it is not always the best indicator of the quality of care. Beware of the 'chandelier effect,' where people assume that high prices and fancy décor are signs of excellent or superior quality. While this may be true sometimes, it is not always the case, and a lovely nursing home may still provide low-quality care.

The **Nursing Home Living Spaces** category looks at furniture, exits, smoke detectors, wheelchair access, and handrails in bathrooms and hallways. Will your loved one share a room? If they have Alzheimer's disease, is a proper alarm system active at the facility?

The **Menus and Food** category helps evaluate food items, special dietary needs, nutritious snacks, and staff help during mealtime. It is also a good idea to make sure that foods fitting the residents' culture are available. The menu should typically include healthier versions of local favorites and be consistent with the demographic of the community. One of the best dumplings I've ever had was visiting a center in Chinatown in San Francisco during a gerontology conference. In much the same way, I would expect the menus in facilities heavily populated by Latinos, such as in the South Bay Region of San Diego, CA, or El Paso, TX, to have rice and frijoles as a staple.

Staffing Levels are of the most important categories on the Medicare checklist. It includes licensed staff on-call twenty-four hours a day, staff-to-resident ratio, respecting the elder's privacy (knocking on doors), turnover in administrative staff, primary language spoken by staff, and staff presence for social service needs. Staff will be interacting with residents regularly and will often be the source of a good or bad experience.

The category **Residents' Rooms** includes items about belongings or furniture in the resident's room, storage space, internet/tv/phone/computer in the rooms, choice of roommates, and security policies and procedures to protect the residents' personal property. Will they share a room with someone else? How are roommates chosen? Can couples continue to share a room if they desire?

The **Activities** category describes available activities, who plans the activities, volunteer programs, visiting hours, procedures to leave the facility for the day, and religious or cultural support. This category helps evaluate how residents can stay active and stimulated during their stay. Do recreational activities include excursions to cultural festivals or your loved one's church? One lovely location in San Diego offers *danzon*, a traditional smooth style of Mexican waltz for its residents.

The final Medicare checklist category is **Caring for Residents with Dementia**. This is an area that I have personal experience with my dad and his DMV incident. Residents with dementia need more specific security policies and procedures to ensure they don't wander off. This area includes the rate and presence of medication use and non-medication-based approaches to treating dementia. Are staff trained and licensed to provide dementia care? Are facilities outfitted with proper alarms on all doors?

Bring the Medicare checklist (or your own, if you prefer) and ask questions about anything you see, hear, or don't understand (this form should be handy in the telephone interview of the nursing home staff too). You should also find the contact person's name and details if you have any more questions. As you can tell, the checklist is comprehensive and is a great starting resource. It would help if you changed it to suit your elder's unique individual needs and preferences. Ultimately, you or a loved one will be living here, so it's crucial to choose a nursing home that will work well.

One great way to get more objective information is to

speak to actual residents themselves during your visit. Ensure to get the resident's permission first (and, if necessary, the resident's family) before speaking to them. You should respect the resident's right to privacy and ask permission to go into the resident's room or any care area. Talking to residents can be a great way to get objective and realistic opinions of the facilities. In contrast, employees have a vested interest in speaking positively about their employer (or face the consequences) and may not always give you accurate information.

Another approach is to attend a resident or family group meeting. The residents and their families organize these meetings to try to fix any issues at the nursing home and improve the residents' experiences. Ask questions about issues that are important to you as a caregiver or elder. Some topics you may want to discuss include:

◊ Recent improvements to improve the quality of life for residents

◊ Plans for future improvements

◊ Nursing home responses to improvement recommendations

◊ Who the group reports to and how often

◊ How membership works

◊ Who is in charge of setting meeting agendas

◊ How decisions are made

Most of these topics center on the customer service side of caregiving in the nursing home and how dedicated the facility is to the residents' quality of life, which are essential details.

Step 4: Choose the Nursing Home that Meets Your Needs

When selecting a nursing home, you want to look at your checklist and carefully review each category. Begin this process by removing the definite Nos from your list. It should be straightforward. Also, set aside the definite yeses. These would be your top picks from the Nursing Home Compare website and Medicare Nursing Home Checklists. Now what you have left are some Maybes.

To help further refine your list of possible nursing homes, you can ask yourself more questions. Some of these may not be on the actual Medicare checklist but are nonetheless important.

⋄ Think about an elder's day and their needs and how these will relate to the nursing home.

⋄ Will their dietary and nutritional needs and preferences be met?

⋄ Will the elder receive adequate preventive healthcare?

⋄ Will the elder's appointments with specialists (dental, ear, nose, throat, podiatrist, ophthalmologist, mental health) are taken care of?

⋄ What type of screening programs for vaccinations are available?

⋄ Can the elder refuse any recommended vaccinations (like the flu)?

⋄ What is the nursing home's policy for the use of antipsychotic medication for dementia treatment? These medications are often overused in these facilities when the staff don't want to be bothered with addressing behavioral issues in other ways.

Then, once you have refined your list further, you can begin looking over your options again. Use a case manager from your local area agency on aging or an ombudsman if they are available to help or ask for advice from others involved in the decision-making process. Once you have a small list, you are comfortable with; it may be worth making one last visit. This time make the visit unannounced and ask to have a look around again. Compare this visit to what you had seen earlier and see if things are consistent or different. You can also bring a trusted friend or family member to help you observe and give their opinion.

Throughout your search, you would've also been exploring your loved one's financial situation and have a grasp of what's covered and what may need to come out of their monthly Social Security check, pension, or other savings. Finally, after all this work, compare your notes again and decide. Speak to all those involved and if you are a caregiver, be sure to get the elder involved throughout this process.

Congratulate yourself on all the hard work and get ready to move in! This is no easy feat. While this process might seem onerous, it is worth all the effort. Plan ahead and begin the nursing home search before you need it, and you will eventually find one that suits your needs. Stay vigilant as the nursing homes may change, and if necessary, choose a new nursing home and get out of the old one.

Services and Approaches that Help with Healthcare

While there are challenges to finding quality healthcare for minorities, there are many resources to help in this search. Like many areas of life, becoming an educated consumer can help caregivers and elders receive better care. The key is to know that these services exist and then find the right one for your needs. Many services aim to help seniors age in place and maintain their independence during their senior years. These community-based care alternatives may be the financial answers elders (predominantly minority seniors) are looking for because they are up to five times cheaper than institutionalization in a long-term care facility (Kaye, LaPlante, and Harrington 2009, Herrera et al., 2013).

The first step is to contact your social worker or case manager (if your loved one is on any governmental assistance program), as they often work for free or on a sliding scale. If you have more financial resources to work with, the Elder Locator website *(https://eldercare.acl.gov)* is an excellent tool to search for a private case manager. These healthcare advocates, often called geriatric care managers (GCMs), help caregivers and elders find the right services and resources for their unique situations. These senior advocates are vitally important as they take on a care planner's role and help coordinate care. Back in 2015 or so, I was at a conference in Virginia where a professional group of geriatric care managers declared a name change to their profession to 'Aging Life Care' professionals. The term 'geriatric care' was deemed to be a turnoff. The new name 'aging life care professional' hasn't quite taken off, so you can search for GCM's on the Aging Life Care Professionals site *aginglifecare.org* or use the search term "geriatric care managers" to find the right person in your area. The two terms are interchangeable.

The Advantages of a Geriatric Care Manager (GCM)

If you are busy and don't have enough time to perform all the functions of a caregiver but have the financial resources, a private GCM may be the answer for you. Often, social workers, psychologists, nurses, gerontologists, or other trained eldercare professionals can play this role on your eldercare healthcare team. Think of a GCM as your quarterback. They have the skills and knowledge to coordinate all necessary logistics and appointments. GCMs have also managed crises, arrange long-term care, and provide daily care assistance. They can even mediate family disputes and provide emotional support! Wow!

With their extensive knowledge and experience in eldercare, GCMs can save elders money as they work to create better outcomes for patients, free up the caregiver's time, and make sure that out-of-state family members don't need to travel as much. Most insurance companies do not pay for this type of private service (and GCMs can cost about $75 - $250/hour), so this is only a good option for people with financial resources.

There are some key things to think about when hiring a GCM, including:

◊ Their education level, licensing, and specialized training

◊ How many years' experience they have

◊ What their fees are

◊ If they receive referral fees for their recommendations

◊ How long the GCM has been in the elder's community (to assess their level of knowledge about local service agencies)

How the Older Americans Act (OAA) Helps

While GCMs can be a great resource to improve the quality of care for elders, their hourly rates can become cost-prohibitive. Instead, you may look at programs funded under the Older Americans Act (OAA) of 1965. This act was signed into law on July 14, 1965, by President Lyndon Johnson. This act, made of seven titles, has laid the groundwork for the resources and services provided to the elderly and aging. The public programs you see today directly result from this act. It is so important that Congress has reauthorized the act in 2016 and 2020 (the act will be valid through 2024). Services and resources such as the Eldercare Locator, Administration on Aging (AoA), and Area Agencies on Aging (AAA) are a direct result of the OAA.

The stated purpose of the OAA is to provide seniors with equal opportunity to the "fair and free" enjoyment of adequate income in retirement, best possible mental and physical health services, suitable housing, long-term care, efficient community services, and freedom independence, and exercise of self-determination. The OAA provides funding for nutrition, home and community-based services (HCBS), health promotion, and other related aging services to achieve these lofty goals for seniors.

The OAA works on a federal level creating a decentralized network of services and resources for the elderly at the local level. Much of the work is delegated to local level organizations, such as your county's **Area Agency on Aging (AAA).** There is now a network of roughly 622 non-profit AAAs nationwide. You'll hear me mention these agencies throughout the book. They are an excellent one-stop-shop to get help with most of your caregiving needs. AAAs are responsible for many of the services described above, along with nutrition (home-delivered meals and congregate meals), caregiver support (including respite care and training), care management, transportation, and long-term care ombudsmen. To find information on your local AAA, use the contact information in the Elder Locator (*https:// eldercare.acl.gov*). You can also search directly online for your local AAA. Search results should be plentiful as there are city, state, and regional AAA websites to help you locate the services that you or an elder needs. Keep in mind that many AAA rename themselves. In San Diego, for example, they are known as the 'Aging and Independence Services.' They often partner with a host of local non-profits to deliver services.

Other Options for Support

Other support services are available at the federal, state, and local levels. If you are unfamiliar with these resources, there are a few places you will want to start your search. The first is *www.Benefitscheckup.org/* which is managed by the National Council on Aging, where I worked for many years. BenefitsCheckUp® screens for over 2,500 public and private programs to help you pay for food, medicine, rent, utilities, and other daily expenses. As described in Chapter 3, the website screens seniors to assess what free or low-cost benefits they may qualify for, based on a series of questions about their medical needs and current financial situation to determine eligibility for each service. The system then generates a list of resources that you can follow up with and often provides you with the application to help you get started. This website is designed to help seniors with limited income and resources to find and use additional services.

Another resource where you can begin your search for eldercare resources is one we mentioned earlier–The Eldercare Locator. You can visit the website at *https:// eldercare.acl.gov (previously: https://eldercare.gov)* or call 800-677-1116 (9 AM–8 PM EST). This is an excellent resource, as it serves as the gateway to eldercare resources. All you need to do on the website is enter the location where you wish to receive eldercare-related services and resources. A list of services in various categories is then generated. Programs and the availability of services vary, so you must check what is offered in your area. Those of you already well into the role of caregiving are familiar with the marathon hours spent online and on the phone with representatives trying to get you the information you need. Don't be deterred.

These two resources are great general starting points for elders and caregivers. However, they don't cover all the available resources. This is especially true for elders who want to age in place or live in their current home. While old age implies a certain degree of dependency on others, many seniors still want to maintain their independence. To help with this, home- and community-based services (HCBS) can provide services targeted at seniors who hope to remain at home. Services such as homemaker, nutrition, and meals, transportation, and energy assistance programs are available for eligible seniors. HCBS can include a particular group of "Medicaid waiver programs," which provide long-term support and services in the home. Such as personal care, housekeeping, chore services, respite care, transportation, medical supplies, equipment, home-delivered meals, cooking, grocery shopping, adaptive technology, and housing modifications. Individuals with low income or a qualifying disability of any age may qualify for these services. Caregivers will also benefit from these HCBSs because they will help take some responsibilities away and give them much-needed time to rest or manage their own lives.

During my research work at the University of Maryland, we found that minority seniors and their caregivers under used such services, despite the higher rates of disability in these populations (Herrera et al., 2013). The primary reason for not using them was the lack of awareness that these services existed. And when they did know about them, some caregivers assumed that elder help was only offered in long-term care facilities. That's not true. The secondary reason was the preconceived notion that one relinquishes their obligations when they resort to seeking outside help.

Many Sources of Public Assistance

Knowing where to look and then using these resources is crucial for helping you get the support you need. However, because of high demand, there is often a lengthy application process, along with long waiting lists. Discussed at length in

Chapter 4, *https://www.Benefits.gov* is a federally sponsored website that can help you search for medical-related benefits and many other types of government programs. These other programs include government loans, disaster relief, veterans' programs, and various local health programs.

Institutional Long-Term Care

Institutional Long-term Care (LTC) is a Medicaid program that pays for nursing homes or similar institutions if you have a medical condition that requires regular skilled care. For help in selecting nursing homes, review the process earlier in this chapter. Many seniors and their families erroneously believe that Medicare will cover any long-term care needs in a facility or elsewhere. That's far from the truth.

Medicare Savings Programs

Another health assistance program is the **Medicare Savings Programs (MSP)**, which is available to those who already qualify for Medicare. To learn more about the ins and outs of Medicare, a highly recommended easy read is the annual guide *Medicaid and You*, the official government handbook. The latest 2021 version can be found here: *https://www.medicare.gov/Pubs/pdf/10050-Medicare-and-You.pdf.* MSP helps Medicare recipients with limited income and assets pay for some of their costs. MSP can pay for a recipient's late enrollment penalty as well. There is a total of four MSPs that Medicare recipients can qualify for:

◊ **The Qualified Medicare Beneficiary (QMB)** program is an MSP that helps Medicare recipients with their deductibles, copayments, and/or coinsurance. If applicable, this can mean QMB pays for Part A and Part B premiums.

◊ **Specified Low-Income Medicare Beneficiary (SLMB)** program and **Qualified Individual (QLI)** program are other MSPs that help pay for Part B premiums.

◊ The final MSP is the **Qualified Disabled and Working Individuals (QDWI)** program for people who are disabled, aged sixty-five or above, and have returned to work (therefore no longer qualify for free Part A). The QDWI program pays for the Part A premiums.

Prescription Assistance Programs

Besides these medical insurance support programs, eligible recipients can also receive prescription help. Medicare Part D is the federal government's prescription medication program, and many plans already offer no out-of-pocket costs to the Medicare recipient. If you must pay a premium for Medicare Part D and have limited resources, you may qualify for Low-Income Subsidy (LIS) or 'Extra Help.' Call your insurance broker and find out details during Open Enrollment.

State Pharmaceutical Assistance Programs (SPAPs) is another program for helping people with limited incomes and savings pay for prescriptions. Some programs will help pay for medications Part D does not cover. Check with your state program to see if you can purchase medications at a reduced price. You can use the search tool at this website to find your state's SPAP: *https://www.medicare.gov/pharmaceutical-assistance-program/#state-programs*

Another option is the **Patient Assistance Programs (PAPs)** offered by drug manufacturers to give those with limited incomes free or discounted medications. You can check this website to find out if you have any qualifying medications: *https://www.needymeds.org.*

Food Assistance Programs

There are also food assistance programs for those in need. The USDA provides food help to those with limited income and resources through a program called the **Supplemental Nutrition Assistance Program (SNAP).** The USDA offers a debit card to allow recipients to purchase food through grocery stores, senior centers, and food programs that deliver meals. Income, housing, utility/medical expenses, household size, and location will determine eligibility and benefits. You can apply for this program through your state's SNAP office. Information about applications and more program details can be found at *https://www.fns.usda/gov/snap.*

The **Emergency Food Assistance Program (TEFAP)** is another option for food assistance. This program helps those with limited incomes and resources purchase basic food items. Fruits, vegetables, cheese, pasta, soups, and beans can be acquired from your local food pantry or soup kitchen. Check your state's programs at *https://www.fns.usda.gov/tefap.*

Another program to help seniors with limited income buy fresh foods is the **Senior Farmer's Market Nutrition Program (SFMNP).** Recipients aged sixty and older with low incomes receive coupons to purchase fresh produce from farmers' markets, roadside stands, and community programs. Not all states have this program, so you will have to check for the program's availability. This program helps needy seniors and promote the use of these local farms. You can more details at: *https://www.fns.usda.gov/sfmnp.*

The final food assistance program we will discuss here is the **Commodity Supplemental Food Program (CSFP)**, which is available in some states. This program provides monthly food packages that seniors over sixty years and with low income can pick up through local agencies. To find more about this program, visit the website at: *https:// www.fns.usda.gov/csfp/commodity-supplemental-food-program.*

Programs for Household Utilities

Household utilities is another area seniors and caregivers can receive help. Various community programs can help, including the **Low-Income Energy Assistance Program (LIHEAP).** This program helps with fuel bills to keep your home cool and warm and prioritizes households with seniors, people with disabilities, and young children. More information can be found at *http://www.benefitscheckup.org /cf/liheap_locator.cfm* or by calling 866-674-6327. Your local utility company will often have discount programs for electric, natural gas, and even phone services. Call them and see what discounts or programs they may have that you can use to your benefit.

Another type of household utility program is the **Weatherization Assistance Program (WAP).** WAP is an energy program designed to make your home more energy efficient by improving the home weatherproofing to make it more efficient to heat and cold. Doing so helps you save money on heating and cooling costs. The WAP program also gives priority to households with seniors, people with disabilities, and young children. More information can be found on the website: *www.energy.gov/eere/wipo/wherer-apply-weatherization-assistance* or by calling *866-674-6327.*

Housing Assistance Programs

Housing assistance is another essential angle, and various programs can help. Before reviewing some of these public programs below, download Kapok's "A Free Guide to Affordable Housing Solutions for Seniors," where we review different housing options, was to qualify for, and factors to consider with these housing options. You can download our free guide, *Kapok's Guide To Affordable Housing Solutions for Seniors,* at *https://www.multiculturalcaregiving.net/a-guide-to-affordable-housing-solutions-for-seniors.*

The federal government's Department of Housing and Urban Development (HUD) can help you find affordable housing. HUD helps people stay in their homes, find apartments for eligible people, find housing units for seniors, and help the disabled.

Section 8 is a well-known program that provides housing vouchers to help pay for your residence. However, because of the program's popularity, there is a lengthy waiting list, and many applicants wait years before being accepted into the program. Section 202 is specifically designed to help seniors find more affordable housing. Later in this book, we'll go in depth about the available housing programs. The Housing and Urban Development website *(https://www.hud.gov/topics/information_for_senior_citizens)* is a great resource to start learning.

Transportation Programs

Being able to get around is an integral part of maintaining an elder's independence. However, as with my father and his dementia, their driving privileges may be eventually revoked due to declining health. Physical mobility can become an issue, and some elders may need specialized modes of transportation to accommodate their wheelchairs or walkers. It's a fact that even when they are quite mobile, some seniors are reluctant to walk in their own neighborhood, afraid of being harassed or assaulted. An AARP Aging Friendly Communities survey revealed that many Hispanic seniors were hesitant to even make quick trips to the store, afraid of being hounded by teenagers in the D.C. urban area. Elsewhere, Asian-American seniors have been the targets of hate crimes, a statistic that rose 150% in 2020 during the pandemic. Can you blame seniors for being hesitant to venture out?

Different programs are available in each community to help seniors get around, including public transportation, volunteer driver programs, private-pay transportation, para-transit, and transportation with assistance. You can search for transportation and local public transit agencies near you at the American Public Transportation Association's (APTA) website: *www.APTA.com*. You can also call your state's 211 info line for more information on transportation services in your area.

Transportation services can vary and depend on your own unique mobility needs. There are some questions you may want to ask before deciding what services to use:

◊ How far can I travel?

◊ Is there a transportation specialist I can speak to?

◊ How long does it take to request a service?

◊ What is the cost?

◊ Are there any limitations to the purpose of my transportation?

◊ Can you accommodate mobility devices?

Be realistic about the limitations of these services. While conducting research during my academic tenure at the University of Maryland, my graduate students and I interviewed Latino, African-American and Korean seniors in senior housing facilities in Maryland about many subjects, including transportation. One senior described his ordeal of having scheduled a surgical procedure, only to wait two hours for his transport to arrive, being driven around town picking up multiple passengers, and then arriving an hour late to for his pre-op check-in. He had to reschedule the procedure and then was on the shuttle for another three hours before finally arriving back home. Can you imagine? Another resident spoke of her heroic efforts to fill a prescription at the pharmacy across the street. Seems simple enough, right? However, this street had incredible traffic and a traffic light that was just too fast for her speed. She needed to coordinate transportation just to fill her prescription across the road.

While minorities are financially disadvantaged in receiving quality eldercare, there are still resources available to help them maintain their independence and lifestyle. If it comes to living in a long-term care facility such as a nursing home, you can follow our four-step process to find a nursing home that meets your family's needs and provides a pleasant living environment. The key to finding additional caregiving resources is to learn where these resources are and then seek them out for the elder's benefit. Websites such as *https://benefits.gov* and *https://eldercare.acl.gov* can be great starting points for finding quality eldercare resources and services.

Chapter 5

Taking Care of Your Finances

As the child of an immigrant family, my family was all too often short on money. Yet, we always stayed within our budget. My mom's greatest talent was stretching a dollar and keeping a tight budget. She knew where to shop for deals and made sure she was never duped. I remember when a yogurt went bad. She marched over to the Safeway and demanded a refund immediately. That's someone looking after their scarce resources. To this day, she writes down all of her expenses and bills; just a simple notebook, no fancy software, no financial planner. Unfortunately, it took me much longer to learn these lessons myself as an adult. I'm here to say that it's never too late. Perhaps motivated by marriage and having a child, I've increased my credit score by almost 300 points in the past five years!

As a young professional just beginning her career, I learned many financial lessons and the related stress of not having enough. I've had to learn about budgeting, saving, taxes, paying down debts, and different ways to earn more money. I've learned that the best way to take care of others is to make sure your financial house is in order first. This way, you have the resources and options available to give to others and have the time necessary to provide needed aid.

Early Financial Lessons

It's easy to settle into the mindset of doing without when you grow up with little; you manage. However, planning for your older years doesn't work like that. We have a saying in gerontology about finances: you're often just 'one away' from crippling debt. You're one crisis away. It may just take one fall down the stairs, one minor stroke, or one car accident that leads to hospitalization to pull you out of your work life and leaves you with a whopping medical bill.

Like some of you, I was taken in by predatory lenders in the 90s. I qualified for FAFSA and got student loans, one after another, all the way through my doctoral program. I avoided them until the lender threatened to garnish my wages. I scrambled to get my act together, and I'm still paying off that sucker today.

I still remember being short of money as an undergrad and signing up for clinical trials conducted by professors at the University of California, San Diego (UCSD). Some studies asked you to identify things on a computer screen, while higher-paying studies put you through more invasive CT scans and MRIs. Still today, I wonder whether being their guinea pig left any lingering side effects.

Later, when I first moved to Albany, New York, for grad school, I had secured an apartment, sight unseen, and when I arrived with my one large suitcase, the apartment didn't even have a light inside. So, the kind Pakistani couple that managed the building helped me run a power cord and lightbulb to my apartment from his place and gave me a meal. That night, I ended up sleeping on a pile of clothes. I thought to myself, *What have I done? Maybe I could have planned this a little better or saved up a little more.* Slowly, as I worked and attended classes, I gained the money to go out and purchase the necessities like a futon and a phone (a landline at the time), and a lamp.

I was one of those people that always claimed to be "too busy" to review my bills and get myself on a budget. When you're this disconnected from reality, you make bad choices that come back to bite you. I bought a Mazda Rx-8 as a reward for myself for finishing the post-grad years and traveled to my heart's content, racking up those credit card bills. Then things got real. I came home one day to find an eviction notice on my apartment door. Having to sell my camera at the pawnshop to make sure I paid rent and had food that month. That got real.

I also had other early financial lessons. I remember having to learn about taxes and when to use a FORM 1099. Learning this tax lesson was a rude awakening and a financial surprise. When you work for an employer, your tax records are reported by the employer to the government.

Well, when you work for any organization that considers you a consultant, that employer is *you!* When you make more than $600 from this business arrangement, you need to fill out a specific tax form, but at the end of the tax year, you get what's called a FORM 1099. For each business/person you work for in the tax year where you make at least $600 from them, you will get a FORM 1099. What's the difference, then? Between 2007 and 2011, my position as a post-doctoral fellow fell into the category of consultant, which relegated me to the 1099 group. I never understood why so many post-doctoral fellowships fall in that category.

The major difference is with the money you receive for the work–taxes are *not* taken out yet as with a regular employer.

That means you will have a lot more taxable income. If you didn't actively set aside an estimated amount each month, you'd have to cough up the equivalent in taxes at tax time. Ignorance about tax law and obligations, unfortunately, is never a good excuse for the IRS. I had to scramble to pay that off for years to come on a payment plan. But these mistakes taught me important budgeting and tax lessons.

Over the years, due to these lessons, my financial situation has improved. Fast forward to 2021, where I have a budget on an Excel spreadsheet. Still, nothing fancy, but it works for us. And alas, we became homeowners last year! My husband and I are not among the fortunate to have wealth or property passed down to them. Financial planning shouldn't be scary. I needlessly avoided it for so long. Getting your finances in order is a key part of living a secure and comfortable retirement.

It wasn't just my personal financial lessons I learned from; other financial lessons were learned when I witnessed countless caregivers sacrifice their financial well-being and become financially 'sick' themselves because of their caregiving sacrifices. With this thought in my mind, I can't imagine caregivers older than me with less earning potential, having to navigate the system trying to find the resources to survive and provide adequate caregiving services for themselves and their own families. The world of caregiving is like the rest of society–the more money you have, the better services you will receive, and the more options you have. The less money you have, the fewer options you will have, especially when deciding on living facilities.

Thankfully, there are ways to improve one's financial situation, whether this involves increasing your income through side hustles, finding ways to save money, planning your finances well, investing, or all of the above. In this chapter, we're talking about key ways to manage finances and stay ahead, starting with the idea of financial planning.

Saving for a Rainy Day

My relationship with money has developed. Maturity and hard lessons woke me up to the reality that avoiding your financial situation was never the answer. Work and family life change over time, and this affects your financial situation. When you are young, your priority may be to work so that you can travel and pay for school. As you get older, your goal might be to own a home or pay for childcare.

At this stage in my life, we are saving and investing for our retirement. My parents never had the means to pay for our schooling, and it's one thing we've vowed to do for our daughter–that is, make sure she never has to worry about student debt. Our attention to finances now has been focused on investing and preparing for retirement and ensuring we have a cushion for an emergency, such as unemployment, or if any of us became gravely ill or needed expensive medical treatment.

It would be best if you thought about how money can contribute to your life's goals and security, and don't be afraid to change up your goals as you move through the stages of life. Don't worry about what others are doing. We started a family much later in life than most people and only recently bought a home. Go at your own pace. At some point, we plan to hit the road in an RV, downsize, and move to some retiree's haven once our daughter is off to college.

You might be asking yourself, "Why work so hard to improve my finances and make more money?" Besides the financial benefits, there are health-related benefits as well. It is well known that financial problems can lead to stress;

with enough stress, disease can be the result. You can literally make yourself sick worrying about your finances. Dr. Tucker-Seeley, a leading gerontologist whose work has centered on financial well-being, has studied the link between finances and chronic disease, especially in the African American community and low-income seniors. Dr. Seeley talks about your financial well-being (FWB) and how it comprises three parts: Material, Psychosocial, and Behavioral (Tucker-Seeley Research Lab, Tucker-Seeley 2008). *What is your relationship with money?*

Material is one's access to financial resources to meet your material needs and "make ends meet." **Psychosocial** is how you feel about those resources. Are you worried about your finances and worried about not meeting your financial obligations? **Behavioral** is what you do with these resources. Do you compare prices before making a purchase? Do you have a plan for how to use your money? Do you follow the plan you make for your money?

Your answers to these questions help identify your level of financial well-being. Dr. Seeley has found that health disparities are linked to socioeconomic factors and that disease (especially cancer) can drastically affect one's financial well-being.

Saving for a rainy day can also be the key to the quality of your caregiving. Imagine the stress you are under from worrying about and focusing on your finances. I get it. I've been there, and it's not fun. How much better can your care and attention to a parent be if you didn't have to worry about your finances? Like my mom (and now me), you can create a simple budget for yourself to make sure your spending is kept in check.

A straightforward way is to write down the 'fixed expenses' that you have every month. These fixed expenses include things like rent, electricity, water, car payments, insurance, groceries, entertainment, and the like. These expenses are what you need to live every month and, in business terms, your monthly 'overhead'—essential expenses to keep your business running. The 'business' in this case is your life. Then, write all of your expected income from your job, side hustles, and investments in a column next to it. This simple method is similar to what my mother did with her notebook, and she was able to take care of our family with this simple system.

Another method of budgeting I learned about and is also quite effective is called the 'envelope technique.' This system is also relatively simple and can be used with the expense tracking system above. What you do is have an envelope that you place cash in for monthly expenses. Grocery shopping, eating out, clothes, and any other discretionary spending you have budgeted goes into this envelope as cash. The cash in this envelope is all you get to spend for that month. After all, it's the discretionary spending that can get out of hand. This method is so effective because you actually get to see and touch the cash you are spending. You also think twice when you can physically see how much you are about to spend and how much you have left. Purchases become more 'real.' You suddenly get very creative with your expenses and are more likely to shop around for a better deal.

Credit card purchases go into your statement each month, and unless you are checking your credit card account every day, you don't always know exactly how much you are actually spending as the month goes on. This untracked spending using a credit card can result in an unexpected surprise at the end of the month. With the envelope method, you know exactly how much you have left to spend for the month.

Of course, it is easier to see your savings grow after you've taken care of your debt. Still, first make sure that you keep at least enough savings to get you through an emergency, approximately three months' worth of living expenses. Once a debt is paid, you can begin using any additional cash to pay other debts. One technique to help you pay down debts is to not focus on the amount of your total debt but on each source of debt. For example, you have three credit cards with balances that you want to pay off. Instead of trying to pay down each credit card each month, you pay the minimum payments for all three of the cards. For the credit card with the highest interest rate, you pay extra money each month until the balance is paid off. Then, once one credit card is paid off, you continue aggressively paying off another card until it is totally paid off. You continue until all the debts on your credit cards are paid off. Prioritize the payoff based on your total potential loss. Beginning with debts that have the highest interest rate, for example, makes wonderful sense. If you have debt collectors already threatening you to tarnish your credit report, then those debts may come first. Always try to protect your credit report, or else you'll diminish your leverage when making future purchases and get penalized with higher interest rates.

One of our financial writers on my Kapok blog used this technique to pay off his student loans. He continued to pay the minimum required balances on all of his loans but paid extra each month on a particular loan he wanted to pay off. Once this loan was paid down to zero, he moved onto the next loan. This technique is more of a psychological trick because you eliminate one source of debt that would otherwise occupy your mind and distract you. Also, as you reduce the number of loans you have, you feel more motivated to continue paying down your other loans because you feel like you are progressing towards your goal of paying down your debt. Eventually, it can be a game where you are having a fun time paying down your debt. I know it sounds gimmicky, but it works!

Ways to Earn More by Increasing Your Hustle

The best way to improve your financial situation is to increase your earning potential or find alternative ways to earn more. Either way, it means you'll have to put in the time–to expand your skills or work serving more clients. Throughout my public health and gerontology career, I always sought additional training to help me stay competitive in the labor force. I'm not getting any younger and need to compete against these millennials. You can take short online courses or squeeze in a seminar when you can. Employers are often flexible and willing to finance your training when you can justify it. With a more competitive skill set, my earning potential has flourished over the years. You may be thinking, "Who has the time for that?" Some of you may struggle to stay in the workforce at all, and we'll address that here. Coaching caregivers on alternative ways to earn money has become a critical part of our strategy in supporting the growing number of caregivers who have to cut down work hours or leave the workforce to stay at home and care for a loved one.

What happens when you need more money? Maybe you have an unexpected health emergency, or you are beginning to run low on cash. What are you supposed to do? What if you are more advanced in age or beginning to feel the subtle effects of 'age discrimination?' Thankfully, as the world begins to embrace the gig economy fully, there are options for you to earn more income. One way is to find your niche and 'side hustle' in the gig economy. From simple to complex, there are gigs you can immediately perform for some extra cash. Childcare, babysitting, and even pet care can offer immediate sources of money with a low barrier to entry. Maybe you're already caring for a grandchild or are a part of a trusted network of parents: you can offer your services to babysit. Some resources to find potential jobs are Bambino, Urban Sitter, Sitter City, Care.com, Trusted, and Rent Grandma. If you're interested in pet sitting, try looking at Wag, Rover, Citizen Shipper, Fetchi, Petsitter, or Care.com.

If you have a reliable vehicle, there is food delivery, which has become all the rage now in the age of COVID-19. Apps and online platforms such as UberEats, GrubHub, DoorDash, and Postmates allow workers a way to earn extra income as well. Whatever your possible side hustle is, just look at your skills and test out how the market responds to your offerings.

Many apps have emerged to support gig workers and are great tools to help you market your services, get paid, and earn short-term income, such as Handy and Task Rabbit. Handy is an app geared towards those who have experience with maintenance work services. Electricians, plumbers, bathroom remodelers, and even home cleaning are services you can provide on this app. You can promote yourself in traditional ways as well, through word-of-mouth and existing social connections. My Uncle Javier, despite his advanced age, complications from his diabetes, and multiple surgeries, has never stopped hustling. He is always doing odd jobs and repairing just about anything from cars to furniture. He became popular with customers when he was a painter and construction worker, and to this day, they call upon him for odd jobs, even if it's just getting his help with hauling away old furniture in his truck.

Below are two links to articles on the Kapok website if you are interested in earning more money:

https://www.multiculturalcaregiving.net/side-hustles-for-caregivers-and-seniors/

https://www.multiculturalcaregiving.net/money-making-hobbies-for-retirees-seniors-and-caregivers/

Ways to Earn More by Selling Stuff

But what if you are an elder and need more cash than you are receiving from Social Security or a pension program and have limitations in your ability to set up a side hustle? What if you need more cash flow? There are more opportunities than you think. One way, as an elder, is to sell unused items. Your house may have furniture, kitchenware, appliances, and even extra cars you are not currently using. Online platforms and apps such as Offer Up + Let Go, 5 Miles, eBay, and Craigslist/CPlus are very well known and user-friendly. Everything from cars to furniture to household items can be sold for cash. With the right product photographs, user reviews, and right product marketing, you can build trust and increase your reach within these platforms. My sister helped my mom post several items from her garage on OfferUp, and it sold during one of my visits. That was cash on hand for my mom for an item that would've otherwise sat in a corner collecting dust. This is also a great way to declutter and downsize.

I have sold many items on both eBay and OfferUp. I maintain a 100% positive rating on my eBay Seller's account. I've sold clothes that my daughter outgrew, including tap shoes and leotards and salad choppers on eBay, and my husband has sold bike parts and old lamps on OfferUp that were taking up space in our garage. The earnings may not be enough to live off of, but over time, the passive income can amount to a month's worth of rent or pay for a nice dinner out. These platforms are popular with buyers and sellers and, depending on what you have to sell, can be a substantial source of extra cash.

YouTube is now filled with sellers who share their tips for turning online selling into full-time work. If you start the downsizing process, you can also turn to these tools to rid yourself of excess possessions to pack up and move. At my caregiving website, we devoted an article to summarize the best apps for selling the belongs that you're ready to part with: *https://www.multiculturalcaregiving.net/best-apps-for-selling-stuff-in-2020/*

I'm now in the process of teaching myself the basics of sewing so that I can make waist and armbands and pouches for my daughter, now that she has both a Continuous Glucose Monitor and hybrid insulin pump that have to be secured to her body. My hope is to share them online and get good enough that others see a value in actually paying for them.

Part of my financial education came from the process of creating and setting up my website, multiculturalcaregiving.net. Everyone has a skill or knowledge base worth sharing. What started as a way to share my knowledge and inspire others has morphed into a part-time project, and I am heavily investing a lot of my current resources into keeping it going. While I love what I do on the website, the reality is I have to work to make it profitable so that it can sustain itself. I'm motivated by the comments we get from readers and inspired by real caregivers to develop new content and ideas for articles. I can't stop! Through this project, I am learning how to manage my team, coordinate projects, and improve the website's cash flow. Maintaining the website has been valuable in adding to my own financial education, and I love all the challenges that come with it.

Investing Your Surplus Cash

Once you've paid down your debts and you're making extra cash through your side hustles, congratulate yourself! You are moving your finances forward, and now the question is, "What do I do with this extra cash?" What you do with your money depends on your goals, but find a financial planner and begin investing your money. Your investment goals will depend on your personal goals, and as you get older, your retirement goals should be your focus. There are many types of financial advice professionals. Still, you will want to find someone licensed, such as a chartered financial consultant (ChFC) or a Certified Financial Planner (CFP). A new class of financial planners called robo-advisors use complex computer calculations to create an investment portfolio based on your goals. For more in-depth information on financial planning, you can visit the Kapok website at *https://www. multiculturalcaregiving.net/financial-planning-for-senior-citizens-what-you-need-to-know.*

Alternative Sources of Cash

Another source of income, especially if you have certain types of assets, is to borrow against them for the needed cash. One such asset is your life insurance plan. Frequently, you may be able to borrow against the cash value balance in the policy, pay the interest to your account, and pay back the principal when you can. This is better than going to a bank because you are paying yourself the interest payments instead of a bank or lender. If this could be an option for you, call your life insurance broker or agent and ask them about the details.

Another option for cash, if you own a home, is a reverse mortgage. Admittedly, there is an ongoing debate on if a house is an asset or not; for the purposes of this discussion, we assume it is because it can provide you with cash flow. If you own a home with equity in it, this may be what you are looking to do. First, a standard mortgage is when you borrow money to pay for a home. On the other hand, a reverse mortgage is when a lender pays you money every month based on the equity you have in the house (equity is the difference between what you owe on the property and the current market value of your home). If you purchased a home, a long time ago and paid off the house (i.e., owe nothing and have no mortgage), this may be an ideal way for you to cash out some of the value of your home. Even if you owe some money on a mortgage, it may be worth it to explore this option.

Hard Lessons

My first lesson with the tax system was shocking. I knew nothing about withholding taxes, nor what a FORM 1099 was. I struggled with my financial well-being, and years later (after much work to learn about taxes and business), I can now navigate the system much better. After all of these lessons, I have come to understand paying down consumer debts and focusing on making more money. Whether you're a caregiver trying to juggle multiple part-time jobs, a full-time employee, or a retiree, as long as you are willing to work, there are ways to make more income creatively through selling your unused household items or finding work in the gig economy.

Chapter 6

Maximizing Your Elder's Resources

As a caregiver, you find it will be easier for you to provide higher quality care to elders once your financial house is in order. With less financial stress and more available mental resources freed up, caregivers can focus on eldercare and help the people they care for maximizing their available resources to provide the best quality of care possible. But to use your loved one's resources efficiently, you need to create a plan based on their current needs and goals. Legal, health, and financial matters will be key components of this care plan and will be discussed in this chapter.

Starting a Care Plan

As self-sacrificing as most caregivers are, their resources are limited; there is only so much one person can do in this world. Caregivers only have so many hours in the day, a finite amount of physical and mental energy, and usually a limited financial resources. As discussed earlier in this book, many caregivers sacrifice their own financial earning potential to perform caregiving tasks and many find themselves shelling out money to cover other care needs for aging parents with little to no savings. Mostly, the responsibility of financing the costs of day-to-day life falls on the older adult. That means they have enough to pay for basic expenses, like food, utilities, rent, and medical expenses. Hopefully, the elder was financially responsible earlier in their life and had adequate resources to help with their care. Some of you may be laughing at that last statement. At best, our parents will have funds for the basics like rent and food, but close to nothing for emergencies or to cover the cost of a home health worker.

Your job as a caregiver is to initiate candid discussions with the older adult early on and move forward with assessing, planning, and having a system in place. They can still make independent decisions or before dementia or Alzheimer's disease begins to show their effects. Once dementia shows up, the elder's decisions may no longer be considered 'legal.' An elder's mental and physical capacity definitely will affect all other phases of their life. If they can't think properly, have a fading memory, or are depressed, their lives will definitely be negatively affected.

Being proactive about the plan is essential to getting the care plan underway, and it begins with tough conversations with the care recipient. If your loved one is still mentally capable, they should be part of the conversation; it's a team effort. Regardless, you must get an accurate picture of their financial health, and you will need to list what needs to be done and what may need more attention. The basic steps of the care planning process include:

Step 1: Start planning with the elder
Step 2: Understanding the elder's goals and needs
Step 3: Gather information
Step 4: Compare current information to desired goals
Step 5: Create a list of what is missing

Step 1: Start Planning with the Elder

The first part of assessing an elder's situation is to have an open and tactful conversation with them. Elders need to be involved in this process because of their unique individual needs. Please don't go rummaging through their bills and personal records without their okay or without proper guardianship. An excellent way to approach this initial step is with the same professionalism that a business might treat its customer. Explain to your parents or family members that you care about them and need their help to provide great care for them.

Step 2: Understanding the Elder's Goals and Needs

Nobody likes to think of themselves as being dependent or vulnerable, not now or in ten or twenty years from now. Remind them that 70% of people who reach age sixty-five will need some professional help to meet their personal care needs (ACL, 2020). To make the scenarios more relatable, bring in examples that are closer to home. You can share personal stories of friends or others who were surprised when a relative suddenly fell ill.

Involve other trusted siblings or relatives, so the senior will understand you're not trying to act in selfish or unilateral terms. But first, you need to understand what they want and need as they age, including as they get closer to the end of life. While it may not be pleasant to discuss one's own death, it is also important to discuss their end-of-life care preferences and concerns while the elder is mentally capable and legally competent to make such decisions.

Step 3: Gather Information

When you have their best interests at heart, who could say no to this? Explain to your family member that you need as much information as possible so that you, the caregiver, can meet their needs. During this conversation, inquire about their legal needs, financial situation, mental and physical condition, nutritional needs, and safety. Some potential information the caregiver may need to include is the contact information for their medical providers, bank account numbers, where they fill their cards, Social Security numbers, and care expectations.

After this initial information gathering, do you have enough details to assess the elder's situation and compare it to what the elder wants? You may need multiple meetings to gather everything you need. Not everyone has the mental endurance to sit through hours of life planning. Just last week, I scheduled a follow-up with our tax agency, as I realized I was zoning out after one hour of talking numbers and documentation. Be sure everyone is engaged, or else set up a follow-up meeting.

Step 4: Compare Current Information to Desired Goals

After the information gathering, you will begin to get a more complete picture of their situation and develop a plan to meet those needs and wants with the available resources. After comparing their current situation with their goals, you write everything down and document it. Later in this book, we review how to create a comprehensive action plan.

Step 5: Create a List of What is Missing

There are various options available to you and the elder as they age. It's your job as a caregiver to connect the dots between their needs and resources out there. As you compile all the essential information to guide the elder's care, you'll quickly become attuned to what's missing. You may need to contact their doctor or pharmacy to get the full picture of their prescription medication, or you may have to pay a visit to the bank with the senior to assess activity on their accounts. If they have expressed downsizing, you can review Chapter 7 to help you understand the options that best suit their needs.

Legal Matters

Disclaimer: Caregivers and elders are recommended to seek the legal advice of a licensed professional for your unique situation. What is discussed in this book is for educational purposes only and should not be considered legal advice.

Part of all these discussions should be the legal aspects of providing care for the elder. Elders may choose to allow you to speak to their physicians on your behalf or not. Healthcare providers and staff must follow the **Health Insurance Portability and Accountability Act (HIPAA)** which provides guidelines to protect and maintain patients' privacy. Without legal authorization from the patient, the caregiver should not be able to access health information or even discuss the elder's medical conditions or treatment with physicians or staff. So, make sure to discuss the topic with the elder.

Many providers are more willing to share information with caregivers in person if they become familiar with them. Some caregivers become familiar faces because they show up often at the elder's appointments and seem intimately involved. It's a bit tougher to gain access to an elder's medical records or request changes to their medication regimen without some formal prior approval and designation as an authorized person. Most medical providers have forms that allow patients to designate individuals authorized to receive health information. Wherever possible, ensure your name is documented in their medical records. In a weird coincidence, my sister, and dad have always had the same doctor for most of their lives. This has made communication easier. My dad's doctor is familiar with my mom, sister, and dad and understands the dynamics between the three of them, but it's rarely this easy with providers. Be sure to get authorization in writing.

One legal aspect of caregiving that should be addressed is the **do-not-resuscitate (DNR)** order the caregiver may face at some point. A DNR is a medical order written by your medical professional on your orders. A DNR states that **cardiopulmonary resuscitation (CPR)** shall not be performed with a cardiac arrest emergency. This does not include directions for any type of mediation or nutrition.

Another type of legal order that a caregiver may face is a **do-not-intubate (DNI).** If you are unfamiliar with medical procedures, intubation is inserting a plastic tube into your windpipe to help with breathing. Once this tube has been inserted, a ventilator is attached to help push oxygen through the tube into your lungs.

A **living will (LW)** should also be drafted. This document tells others about what you want to have done regarding your medical treatment, including medications and procedures to prolong your life. The LW becomes effective when you are unable to communicate and are still alive. A situation such as an elder in a coma can invoke their living will. While an LW reflects an elder's wishes in the past, sometimes situations may change, and an LW may not reflect an elder's most recent decisions.

Speak with the elder about designating a **medical power of attorney (MPA),** to represent an elder's most recent decisions. It is a legal assignment that appoints a medical representative (a.k.a "health care agent") of the elder's choosing. The MPA allows the medical representative to make medical decisions on behalf of the elder's best wishes, often based on the most recent input from the elder. This can be more flexible than the living will and other types as it allows for real-time decision-making instead of relying on an old (and possibly out-of-date) document.

Speaking to a licensed legal professional is advised, but the discussion can also be started with your elder's health care professionals. What is essential is to have a plan in place to respect the wishes of the elder. These decisions can always be reversed or updated, so don't be afraid to speak to elders regarding these legal orders; it's in their best interest to document how they want their end-of-life care to proceed. Most importantly, be sure to update these regularly. This could be every two to five years, or even more frequently, such as every six months if their health is more fragile.

Health Issues

During your information-gathering phase, you will also be able to judge the elder's health condition, which includes their mental and physical health. Often the caregiver is taking care of a family member daily, so a caregiver should be able to notice changes in mental and physical health–if they know where to look for symptoms. This is another reason to speak to the elder's health team (physicians, nurses, or other caregivers) to determine ongoing health problems and what to look for when the mental and physical decline occurs. Documenting all of this allows the caregiving team to be up to date. It's crucial to take note of health changes following newly prescribed medications after a hospitalization or emergency room visit. Major events that require emergency care typically come with significant changes to a senior's arsenal of medications. Unfortunately, a new batch of medications can lead to adverse effects, sometimes toxic or life-threatening.

Dementia is a common type of mental deterioration, with Alzheimer's disease being the most common, and dementia isn't a normal part of aging. Dementia can begin to show up in everyday activities such as basic hygiene, eating food, and social interactions. During the information-gathering phase, it is vital to ask about the elder's health conditions and observe for any signs of mental deterioration. Also, speaking to the elder's healthcare providers is an excellent source for this type of information.

Some signs of Alzheimer's are memory loss (especially recently learned information), language issues (forgetting simple words), disorientation, and changes in mood or personality. These are examples of cognitive decline and should be carefully monitored for signs of progression. Alzheimer's disease (a common form of dementia) may not seem like a severe disease–at first. But imagine an elder who forgets who they are and where they are. Then, the elderly person wanders off and disappears. When family and friends realize the elder has disappeared, panic ensues. This is a common scenario, and often this elderly person ends up on the news hopefully, found safe and sound. For caregivers taking care of elders with dementia, the role is no small feat. The data shows that about an estimated 21.9 hours of care per week is given to family members and other unpaid caregivers of people with Alzheimer's disease and other dementias (Alzheimer's Association, 2015). An earlier study reports nine hours per day of caregiving to family members with dementia (Fisher et al., 2011). Caring for a family member then becomes a solid part-time job. Like I said earlier, it takes a special person to be a caregiver–especially when caring for someone with Alzheimer's.

When you combine caring for an elder with Alzheimer's disease and another common health condition, incontinence, you have the requirements for an even more challenging caregiving arrangement. Imagine an elder who does not remember where or who they are and then also cannot recognize the signs of needing to use the bathroom. This can be disastrous. Incontinence can increase in the later stages. Generally, incontinence is the release or leaking of bodily excretions due to various reasons. There are two main categories of incontinence–urinary incontinence and bowel incontinence. As a caregiver, this is a meaningful conversation to have with elders because there are tools and various ways to treat incontinence. This topic may be a little embarrassing, so going about this conversation in a light-hearted but matter-of-fact way can help put the senior at ease. An open line of communication should result between the caregiver and the elder.

Many factors can help cause incontinence, so gathering as much information during the assessment phase can help evaluate what measures may be taken at home and what may need to be discussed with the elder's healthcare professionals. Health conditions that can contribute to urinary incontinence include obesity, diabetes, Alzheimer's disease, hysterectomy medications, menopause, and prostate problems. Lifestyle factors such as diet, water consumption, weight, smoking, caffeine, and alcohol consumption are also contributing factors to urinary incontinence. Bowel incontinence, similar to urinary incontinence, has various medical causes: diarrhea, muscle, or nerve damage from childbirth, hemorrhoids, and multiple medications. Lifestyle factors, such as physical inactivity and diet, can contribute to bowel incontinence too.

Suppose symptoms or contributing medical conditions of incontinence are present. In that case, special care may be taken to help prevent or minimize the effects, but the effort must be made to discover this information. Documenting these conditions will help the caregiver's job tremendously and allow the caregiver to be proactive to minimize the effects of the eventual 'accident.'

Incontinence can be made worse by the elder's mobility issues. If there is an urge, but the elder cannot get to the toilet quickly, or they forget where it is, this delay can result in an accident. When speaking to the elder, discuss any previous injuries or current physical impairments and document these conditions as well. If symptoms or conditions are present, that may cause incontinence, there are continence aids for the proactive caregiver. Many of these aids are commonly available to purchase on popular online platforms. For example, some clothing will have velcro fasteners or a range of commodes that reduce accidents.

While we primarily cover issues around dementia and incontinence here, they provide a prime example of how the senior's health issues can affect their day-to-day care management. There are many other health challenges, too— each of which requires the same level of research, care, and attention by the caregiver.

Money, Money, Money

When gathering information to assess an elder's financial situation, it is crucial to list expenses and assets together to determine the level of financial resources. Financial assets alone don't paint the complete picture. You need to determine if the lifestyle they expect to live with those assets is realistic. You may be the first person in their life to be asking the tough questions: "Can they afford to live here?" and "Can they afford to keep that car?" Whatever you do, give them a break if there's a significant mismatch between what they want and what their wallet will allow. We've all been there at some point in our lives–living beyond our means until creditors put a stop to it. Now, I would love to pay for a cleaning crew to come help twice a month, but we've chosen to use that money to pay for my daughter's Taekwondo class that teaches her discipline, strength, and self-defense. I'm a big fan of the Tesla, too–boy, are they sleek! I can just picture myself cruising through the desert mountains in a Tesla. Instead, I've traded in the flash for my very economical Hyundai Elantra. It comes with comfortable monthly car payments and is good on gas. Budgeting for your lifestyle is going to be filled with trade-offs. But even with a less than ideal financial situation, there are different programs to help support elders with some of the basics.

Social Security and assets like a 401k or stocks may serve as important sources of income. You will need the elder's birthday and their working history to assess their eligibility for Social Security. There are some simple rules to determine eligibility, but the various situations can be a little confusing. Luckily there are tools available on the official Social Security website (www.ssa.gov), and you can also search for related articles on our multiculturalcaregiving.net website.

Assessing the elder's eligibility is a good starting point for planning what needs to be done before retirement age and strategically planning their retirement. The first assessment of Social Security is to make sure the elder qualifies. With Social Security, a worker must have earned at least 40 credits with at least $1,410 in earnings for each credit. Most people will earn at least $1,410 in the span of three months. Four credits (or one credit per quarter) is the maximum amount earned per year, so it takes at least ten working years to qualify for Social Security benefits. But that is just the minimum qualifying amount. The elder's Social Security entitlement, once qualified for, is calculated using the top thirty-five income-earning years.

The best time to retire and begin receiving Social Security depends on the elder's unique personal situation. An important question to answer is, "When does the elder need their Social Security money?" If the answer is "soon," the elder may opt for early retirement, giving them a smaller monthly payment. But suppose the elder does not need Social Security benefits. In that case, they can wait until age seventy to maximize their monthly benefit and continue working for income, and continue contributing to Social Security. The earlier someone takes Social Security, the less their monthly benefits/money will be. For 2020, the maximum retirement benefits for age sixty-two (Early Retirement) was $2,265/month. At age sixty-five (Full Retirement), it was $3,011/month. At age seventy (Late Retirement), it was $3,790/month. (This information was obtained via *https://www.ssa.gov/benefits/calculators*). We touch more on Social Security in Chapter 3, Chapter 6, and throughout this book.

During the financial information phase, it is a good idea to look at the elder's monthly financial needs. An elder with a home paid off, and a healthy retirement account will have drastically different financial needs than someone with no retirement benefits which is still renting an apartment. Gather information, including items such as rent, food, utilities, insurance, gas, internet, phone, data, medical consumables, entertainment, and other expenses. These expenses, when added up, will help the caregiver assess how much is required to survive. Once this has been determined, and the elder comes up short, they can find different ways to earn more to make up for the financial shortfall. But hopefully, the elder has worked and saved enough that there will be enough–you have to think positively!

Fortunately, even with a financial shortfall, Social Security benefits recipients can still work and earn even while "retired." While 70% of seniors expect to need to work past retirement, only about 26% of retirees need to do so (41 Best Retirement Statistics & Facts 2020 | Retirement Is All On You).

Seniors who have retired at their Full Retirement Age can earn up to $18,420 before having $1 deducted from their benefits for every $2 earned above this threshold. If the senior earns more than $48,420, $1 is deducted for every $3 made over this threshold. So if only a small amount of extra income is required per month, the senior can take up a part-time job to earn income and stay active in the community. This part-time job can help prevent the social isolation that is common amongst retirees and contribute to better mental health. Chapter 5 is filled with ideas for bringing in more money. Otherwise, family members with the means may decide to split the cost and pitch in a certain amount to offset these expenses.

Making these types of critical decisions requires accurate information about the elder's working life. Tax returns and old pay stubs can be valuable sources of information gathered from elders. Once you have gathered all the elder's financial records, you can head over to the Social Security website to estimate benefits (https://www.ssa.gov/benefits/calculators).

While this is an estimate, it will give you a general idea of the benefits to be received. Then, the elder can decide how much is needed and how much to make up each month.

Some elders, instead of retiring, continue to work well into their seventies. Retirement for many becomes a time of lost purpose and social isolation if they are not proactive about preparing for this eventuality. The elders who continue to work may or may not be performing their 'encore.' It's in their 'encore' years that seniors are said to be doing the work and job they love on their terms. But working this 'encore' job can only really be enjoyed and revered if you have the option to work–and doing so is not a financial necessity. These workers work because they enjoy what they are doing and the social participation. And with more work and the mental stimulation associated with it, seniors can keep their minds sharp. Who would want to give up all of these work benefits for idle time at home by themselves? Although the 'full retirement' age is sixty-seven for those born on or after 1960, the current average retirement age is sixty-three for women and sixty-five for men. The average retirement lasts eighteen years, and this may be a long time to spend idly, especially if you are used to a busier, active schedule spent challenging your mind and body.

Regardless of what is happening with Social Security today, one day in the not-too-distant future, the retirement age may increase to seventy as people's life expectancy continues to increase, and the funds in the Social Security trust begin to dry up. Every Congress and new Administration bring up changing the eligibility to improve the solvency of Social Security. People will need more working years to pay into the current Social Security trust fund to qualify for any payout.

Chapter 7

Housing and Living

Housing is one of the most crucial parts of any retirement plan. For most people, accommodation will be a major, if not the largest, part of one's monthly expenses. And, as discussed earlier, conducting a financial assessment is a critical way to give the caregiver a good idea of the senior's monthly income and fixed expenses. Knowing the senior's cash flow will allow you to determine how much they can afford to pay for housing. Of course, affording something and wanting something are two entirely different concepts. They may want a high-end retirement lifestyle, and they can have it–*if* they can afford it.

Back East, a friend and I a stepped in to help a woman in her early sixties in our building who was being evicted. She ignored the postings on her door for too long. When we began assessing her resources to help her find a dwelling more suited to her income, it became clear why she hadn't settled on a new apartment. She wanted a place right along the main bus lines with large square footage, renovated kitchen, and so on. Once we walked her through her search options for her desired regions, she realized that all she could afford, at best, was a spare room in someone's home. We ultimately got her to think about relocating to the outskirts of the city. She was also unemployed and in search of work, so the new target area became the perimeter for her job search. Later, I was surprised to receive a call from her daughter who was more than willing to take her in. The daughter was genuinely shocked that her mother didn't seek out her help in this crisis. Ultimately, she stayed with her daughter until she was able to get processed for discounted senior housing.

The numbers revealed during your assessment will tell the financial story and help determine what they can reasonably afford for the services they require. Location matters when talking about housing. This chapter will review different housing options and programs that will help with the planning for housing during the elder's golden years.

What Type of Help is Needed?

As part of an elder's assessment, the caregiver should have a crystal-clear understanding of their level of independence. Can they put their shoes on? Prepare their own meals? Remember to take their medications? As the caregiver, it is helpful to have good documentation of the elder's current health conditions and daily regimens, what medications are being taken, and what types of regular treatments are needed. This will inform the kind of services that need to be in place and narrow down the list of appropriate facilities or retirement home environments. For example, seniors requiring ongoing physical therapy or dialysis may need specialized medical staff or facilities. Housing options will be very different for seniors who can still safely live independently than those who need daily support.

Another key consideration is the senior's ability to get around town. The on-site transportation services offered at some facilities may be beneficial and attractive for seniors with limited mobility. Your loved one may be reasonably physically mobile but no longer drives or feels uncomfortable driving during rush hour or to downtown medical facilities. Some facilities have their own van services, while others contract with transportations service providers. Still, having staff on-site to arrange for an Uber or Lyft ride is a big plus.

These types of medical and lifestyle factors should be considered when choosing where to live. A common assumption is that the only forms of alternative residences for seniors are skilled nursing facilities. This is on the far end of a wide range of options. If you've determined that your loved one won't reside with you, please know that there are many housing options to choose from, with prices ranging from affordable senior apartments to luxury retirement communities. Some options are within the public sector, while others are private facilities instead. Some have on-site residential managers that check in on seniors, while others are more fully equipped with medical staff. This chapter will start with the assumption that you've gathered basic information about your loved one's medical conditions, mobility, and needs.

Location, Location, Location

Many elders choose to stay near family and friends to maintain their social connections, and with good reason: old age can become lonely without social ties. Moving to a new location means that the senior needs to develop new social connections and friendships. Making a move might be worth it for people who want a new living environment, a warmer climate or have some other incentive to move. Still, it is essential to weigh the pros and cons of each option before deciding the best place to live.

While many elders decide to stay or move near their social groups, others may choose to be more adventurous and decide to move back to their country of origin and retire. While this move may look great on the surface, every option presented has its pros and cons. In Chapter 8: The International Caregiver, we speak more about the unique circumstances of caregivers who support seniors living abroad and the pros and cons of considering relocating them closer to your own community. The grass may sometimes appear to be greener elsewhere, but often it is not.

The lower cost of living in their home country may be one reason for returning, but there are just as many limitations and other variables to consider. For example, the infrastructure may not be as developed, medical standards of care may be lacking, and feelings of depression may creep in because of being socially isolated.

The rule of law and ethical standards may be lacking in certain countries. The **Corruption Perceptions Index (CPI)** *(https://www.transparency.org/en/cpi/2020/index/us)* is a reasonable estimate of public sector corruption and may be a wonderful resource to reference before deciding to move abroad. Mexico, for example, is ranked 124th out of 180 countries in terms of corruption in the public sector. Not to mention the violence. After my cousin was kidnapped and held for ransom in 2007, we learned firsthand how a country whose government is controlled by the cartels in many places could instill unfathomable fear and anger and have a way of eating away at your mental health. My aunt and uncle suffered unimaginable stress and heartache during that time. We were lucky that he returned home, albeit emaciated and with long-lasting post-traumatic stress disorder, but others were not so lucky to have their family member or friend return at all.

After being used to the relatively good rule of law in the U.S., the truth is that few ever make that return home because it's no longer home. Most of their closest relatives may have also moved to the U.S. Returning to their country of origin is an idea they discard after more deliberation and thought.

From a caregiver's perspective, it's also challenging to manage your parent's real estate, properties, or health if they live in another country. My dad, for example, owned a very small property in Mexico. None of my sisters or I were willing to make the regular trips to check on the property and deal with tenants. We initially dealt with crooked court clerks, and the property was ultimately illegally seized. Would the outcome have been different if my father was in Mexico to manage the property? Perhaps.

Given my dad's advanced dementia, the family decided to let the property go and put it behind us. This is an example of unintended consequences and situations we are not used to here in the U.S. Only after carefully weighing the pros and cons of retiring overseas should an elder make an informed decision. But even if my dad would have been able to hold on to the property, with his advanced age and ailing health, would he have been able to return 'home' to sell the property? Maybe, but most likely not. Granted, my father's real estate adventure is an anecdotal experience I am sharing, but the message should be, "Is it safe to retire here? Is the rule of law enforced, or is corruption the norm/very common?" The result may have been different in a different country and under other circumstances. But this was my family's experience with real estate in Mexico, and, as mentioned earlier, the Corruption Perceptions Index validates my family's experience. Of course, your experience may vary.

My grandfather owned a Mexican bakery in Rosarito, across the border in Mexico, for many years. Well into his 80s, he traveled almost daily to check in on his business. As he became ill, my aunts ultimately passed along the business and property to the loyal employees who had operated the business for decades. They simply could not manage the company and their personal lives in the U.S.

Besides these real estate adventures, any elder's retirement enjoyment may depend on their ability to carry on with those things that bring them joy, such as entertainment and activities or visiting with grandchildren. These may play a role in the ideal retirement location too. For example, an elder may enjoy walking near the beach, take part in regular trips to the casino (as my dad and grandmother had in common), or enjoy the availability of their favorite cuisine and friends that speak their language, not to mention the weather! Many snowbirds come to Arizona from wintry parts of the country to thaw out and enjoy the sun. My in-laws back in Maryland have a hard time shoveling their snow, and they can't wait to get away to warmer weather.

And finally, the most significant factor in choosing where to live is money, the almighty dollar. More money allows elders to select from more services and experience a higher standard of living during retirement. Social Security's average monthly entitlement payment for 2019 was $1,461 per month. This average translates into $17,532 a year. Renting just a low-income apartment usually requires at least

$19,000/year in income. This does not factor in cash for basic living necessities: food, electricity, water, gas, insurance, and medical expenses. Having a budget and writing down these items will give the caregiver and elder a good idea of what is needed just to survive. The key question an elder should ask themself is not what they want but what they can afford. And this is all based on the elder's monthly budget. As the saying goes, "Money makes the world go-'round."

Around the world, social networks and communities thrive when they support younger and older members of their society. That interdependence isn't looked down upon as a weakness; it may even be celebrated as a strength, and having the extended family involved may be the norm. However, in the developed Western world, achieving independence is not only a goal: it's often used in aging and social services as a way to describe an older adult that is thriving. People in the U.S. are terrified of appearing to need others' help or on anyone to support their lives. It's not uncommon to hear seniors express their wish never to have to rely on their children as they age. The facts, however, don't line up with this expectation. A large proportion (70%) of seniors over sixty-five will need some level of long-term care during their lifetimes. Of these seniors, 42% of elders over the age of eighty-five will need long-term care services (ACL, 2020)

If you're reading this book, you've likely determined that someone in your close circle needs some degree of assistance with activities, such as bathing, dressing, and eating [activities of daily living (ADLs)] or light housekeeping, laundry, and meal prep [instrumental activities of daily living (IADLs)]. A caregiver must consider what services and amenities they need to determine if looking for outside help is the best choice for their situation. Some questions to consider when deciding if assisted living is the correct choice for the care recipient:

◊ Have they recently experienced a fall?

◊ Do they find it challenging to move from one room to the next?

◊ Do they struggle with preparing healthy meals or with getting enough to eat?

◊ Do they accidentally leave appliances on or forget that they were using the stove?

◊ Are they able to pay their bills effectively?

◊ Are they struggling to take care of themselves or their home?

◊ Can they afford in-home help for the hours needed?

◊ Can family or friend provide enough in-home help for free to fill the gap?

Caregivers that answer yes to one or more of these questions should seriously consider the need to find an **assisted living facility (ALF).** Perhaps you or another family caregiver is experiencing your own health or financial crisis and can no longer provide the level of in-home care needed, and the cost for paid help is beyond the elder's budget or yours. You may not need all amenities and services provided by the typical ALF. Still, their services begin to address the issues you've identified and promote the overall health and safety of your loved one. For more information on assisted living for seniors, you can visit the Kapok website at: *https://www. multiculturalcaregiving.net/myths-and-realities-of-assisted-living-for-seniors.*

The multitude of affordable housing options can be confusing. We created the "Affordable Housing for Seniors" resource available at *https://www.multiculturalcaregiving.*

net/a-guide-to-affordable-housing-solutions-for-seniors/. In this housing resource, we review each type of housing and the many individual factors that will influence their suitability for elders. Housing programs also vary considerably in their eligibility requirements by state or region. There are different housing types available depending on the program you're looking at; Income level, age, functional level, and disability status will be the key factors that will drive your choices. This makes it critical to look at the specifics in your local area before deciding.

In terms of specific residential care facilities for elder caregiving, there are four major categories:

1) Independent Living

2) Assisted Living Facilities/ Communities

3) Nursing Homes

4) Continuing Care Retirement Communities

Independent Living (IL) facilities are for highly functional elders who would like minor aid in their day-to-day lives. These types of facilities include single-family homes and townhouses with private security and social activities. Amenities provided may comprise laundry services, meals, transportation, and social activities.

Assisted Living Facilities (ALF) are typically communities in a two to three stories tall building. These types of facilities provide twenty-four-hour security and more ADL services than IL facilities. While similar to IL, it is the aid in bathing, dressing, toileting, housekeeping, medication, assistance, and emergency calls that separates them from their IL counterparts. 24-hour medical services are not provided here.

Nursing Homes are the next level up from ALFs as

they provide many of the same amenities as ALFs, with the difference is that medical care is available twenty-four hours a day and the ADL services.

Continuing Care Retirement Communities (CCRC) are the ultimate retirement housing option. These resemble large campus-like communities providing a continuum of care, ranging from private residences to AL to memory care to skilled nursing care. This type of residence is ideal for elders with declining health conditions.

More Housing Options

In addition to these residential care options for elders, other housing types may be available to seniors.

Senior Housing

The first type of housing for elders we will review is **senior housing**. Senior housing refers to types of homes with age restrictions on who can live in them. Such housing options are supported under a local, state, or federal program and may also receive government funding.

This type of housing ends up being more restrictive than many other options. This can be a good thing, as it limits the number of potential applicants. Housing communities can specialize in the needs of seniors by limiting the profile of residents. Sometimes, senior housing facilities can also make selections based on family criteria. For example, a senior housing complex may place priority on residents above a certain age.

Some housing complexes may only cater to single seniors or couples and may not accept a larger family unit, which would exclude a senior caring for a grandchild. In other cases, a complex may not accept residents under a certain age.

There are two specific brackets of senior housing provided under the Housing for Older Persons Act (HOPA). The first of these is for persons aged **55+ years.** Housing under this category must meet the following criteria:

◊ 80% of units contain at least one person aged fifty-five or above

◊ The property must follow age verification processes

◊ Must both publish and follow policies that state its focus on providing senior living

These criteria make it possible for families to live in housing if only one member is older than fifty-five. Additionally, families could also live there even without someone over fifty-five if they were able to secure one of the 20% of units not required to have such a person. This means that **55+ housing** tends to be less restrictive.

The second category is **62+ housing.** Here, as you might expect, the focus is on seniors aged sixty-two and above. However, the primary criterion is different, as all residents need to be aged sixty-two or above (except for disability-related caregivers). The other two criteria remain the same: the property must follow age verification processes, and it must both publish and follow policies that state its focus on providing senior living. Because of this, 62+ housing is best suited to individual seniors or couples who are both at least sixty-two years of age.

Both types of facilities may look and feel like regular housing communities. Some can be gated and resemble normal single-family and townhouse communities. The only difference is the age restrictions. These types of properties are readily seen on websites catering to online real estate sales listings. Popular sites like Zillow.com or Redfin.com should have listings from these types of communities, so a search can help you see what is on the market. A potential drawback of these facilities is that they might be harder to sell because of the community's age requirements. The 55+ and 62+ age markets have smaller markets than homes with no age restrictions. However, for a senior looking for social connections with other elders, this may be a good option.

Public Housing

Another housing option for seniors with low income is **public housing.** Public housing is a broad term describing government-subsidized housing, with Section 8 and Section 202 being the most popular and well-known. These are prevalent programs as they provide financial assistance to those who meet specific eligibility requirements. The following information is crucial when applying for any housing assistance:

◊ Annual gross income

◊ Whether you are considered a family, an elderly or a person with a disability under the criteria for the program

◊ Your immigration status/citizenship status

◊ Names and pertinent details of all family members who would live in the housing

◊ Current phone number and address

◊ Characteristics and circumstances of the

family that might help them to qualify (such as currently living in poor quality housing)

◊ Names and contact information of previous landlords

◊ Estimate of expected income for the following twelve months

◊ Names and addresses of banks, employers, and anyone else relevant for verifying income, deductions, and family composition

Information on the application will be verified, and someone from a public housing authority (PHA) may visit the family to interview family members.

Section 8 of the Housing Act of 1937 supports the government paying rental assistance to private landlords. Essentially, it allows low-income tenants to afford housing because the government is paying part of the rent.

A key part of Section 8 is the **Housing Choice Voucher Program.** This program provides rental help on a tenant basis. This allows tenants to shop around for the unit of their choice, and if they move to another unit, the voucher follows them. The apartment or unit must meet minimum quality standards for tenants to use their vouchers to cover the rent. People can put their vouchers toward the cost of purchasing a home in some situations. For many people, Section 8 vouchers are a gold mine for finding affordable housing. Perhaps the most significant advantage of these vouchers is that they open up housing options. For seniors, the vouchers can make it possible to find housing outside the umbrella of senior housing. In general, the amount of help provided through these vouchers is based on the normal amount required to rent a moderately priced unit in your specific area. Your county's housing authority determines this with approval by the federal program.

Eligibility for Section 8 is ultimately determined by the PHA based on the family size and the gross income for the family. Section 8 is also largely limited to U.S. citizens, although some groups of non-citizens may be eligible. Normally the income of the family must not be over 50% of the median income for whatever metropolitan area or county that the family lives in. However, most Section 8 vouchers go to families who earn 30% or less of the median income for that area.

Some vouchers may go to families considered low income, which is less than 80% of the median income for that area. However, this group is given the lowest priority. A family's eligibility is determined through an application process through the PHA. This process involves examining a range of information, including income, family composition, and assets. That information is also verified through external sources. If you were found eligible under Section 8, then you would probably be put on a waiting list until the local PHA had the resources to assist you.

To get started in this process, visit your local public housing authority office for information to apply. Drawbacks to such a popular program are the long waiting lists and time to receive benefits (if at all). Applicants can expect to wait *years* before getting lucky in a lottery drawing. And with the national affordable housing crisis and the state of the economy, the waiting list can last even longer as more and more people are facing financial hardships.

Another federal housing program, **Section 202 of the Housing Act of 1937**, is geared toward low-income seniors over sixty-two years of age. The housing is designed for individuals who wish to live independently but need support in some key areas, like bathing or dressing. The living environment can provide more support than other types of senior housing.

The key requirement for Section 202 is that the head of household is at least sixty-two years of age. Proof of income is required, along with proof of age. Other household members can be younger than sixty-two, but they are included in the income calculation.

Applications need to be made individually to each Section 202 property that you are interested in; because demand is high, many of these properties have a waiting list, which you may be on for a year or more before landing a residence.

Funding for the program has been relatively limited, so this type of housing is not available in all areas. However, in 2019, the Department of Housing and Urban Development announced new funding for the program, providing $50 million in funding. This is the first new funding for the program since 2010. This funding should mean that there is more housing available under Section 202 in the future. It also suggests the program may receive more funding in later years. Section 202 is especially important as there are no other affordable housing programs that focus on seniors alone.

Naturally Occurring Retirement Communities

The final housing option to be discussed here is called a **Naturally Occurring Retirement Communities (NORCs).** These types of housing communities don't start out as deliberately planned senior communities. They just "naturally" become communities as residents begin to "age in place," and retirees move into a building or neighborhood and make up a majority of the residents. Most NORCs are publicly and privately funded entities and provide various services typically for a smaller fee than assisted living facilities, independent living facilities, and nursing homes. Publicly funded NORCs can include funding from the county, state, and federal programs.

What's neat about NORCs is that you can essentially start your own. Perhaps you've noticed that your aging parents' neighbors are all experiencing the demands of aging. What if all the adult children got together and agreed to pay for a formal caregiver or care companion to make their rounds on their block on an agreed-upon schedule at a set rate? One of the toughest parts of a home health worker's job is the challenge of having to string together several part time jobs. The group approach would be attractive to a home health worker looking for secure, ongoing work. I've often thought about doing this in my parents' own neighborhood. My mother's neighbors on the street all have shared needs for occasional rides, help with basic cleaning needs around the house, and someone with more advanced care needs in the home. Some services needed are already in house, you could say. My parents' neighbor is a gardener with a young family, who makes his way up and down the block cutting the grass and trimming bushes for the seniors on his radar, and my sister pays him when she visits. Don't be afraid to check with your own parents' neighbors to see if such an arrangement might be attractive.

Your home is your sacred ground. This doesn't change as you age. Seniors want a home that, besides being affordable, is their refuge. They feel comfortable and safe. If you are closely monitoring the senior's health and well-being, their changing needs for different housing should not come as a surprise. They'll have more options if you can expect this in advance and avoid getting caught scrambling for housing options.

Chapter 8

The International Caregiver

Caring for aging parents overseas or across the border in their home country is a surefire way to add complexity to your caregiving duties. Sending remittances (money), coordinating care, navigating a foreign system, and monitoring aging loved ones can be done, but the processes will take more effort than if they were living nearby. Moving aging parents or elderly family members to your country has probably crossed your mind many times, or you may be in the middle of this process now. Doing so can help make caregiving easier. Your understanding of the health care system and available resources in your home country can make moving the elder to you a significant advantage in the caregiving process.

In the perfect world, you should start the process for this international move while the senior is in fair physical and mental health so they can withstand the stress. Also, international moves take a lot more logistical maneuvering, and the immigration process can be lengthy and daunting.

Depending on the age when you moved to the U.S. and how often you visited your or your parents' home country, it may be an entirely different world, and staging the move can become overwhelming quickly. When my family moved an aunt and uncle, who were already U.S. citizens, from Mexico to the U.S., the entire process took at least a year before he was finally settled in a senior living community.

Sending Money Abroad

Whether you are contemplating moving your parents to the U.S. or not, they may still need financial assistance while living in another country. An excellent way to help is to send money, or remittances, abroad. If you are unfamiliar with the term, a remittance is a transfer of money over international borders. With some resources and careful planning, it should be possible to send money to a loved one affordably. As you plan to send remittances, you'll want to get familiarized with your loved one's living situation abroad. Are they surrounded by trusted family or friends? Can they comfortably get to and from the bank without worrying that someone will take advantage of them? Is there a risk that some negative forces in their circle would attempt to keep part or all that money for themselves–whether it's the driver, the banker, or their housemate?

With today's high-tech financial system, sending money should be pretty straightforward if you are versed in using apps and the internet. But what if your family member is opposed to this technology? Or what happens if the elder lives in very rural or isolated areas and the broadband is spotty or nonexistant?

There are many options for sending remittances, and each

has its pros and cons. In this section, we will assume your loved one is not too tech-savvy and may need some low-tech solutions to receive the money.

Keeping these challenges of sending remittances in mind, the first way to send remittances abroad is very low-tech–snail mail. You can send old-fashioned personal checks, traveler's checks, money orders, and even cash (from the U.S. Postal Service) abroad for a relatively cheap fee. Traveler's checks, while not as popular as before, can also be mailed. The biggest drawback is the likely delay in accessing the money from these financial instruments so that the bank can clear the funds. Planning early and sending the remittances before they are needed will be the key to maintaining this lifeline to your elders. Cash can also be mailed, but check with your local laws regarding sending cash as many countries have regulations regarding limits on sending financial instruments across borders.

Easy Ways to Send Cash in the Digital Age

Another relatively low-tech way to send cash remittances is through Walmart. For a relatively modest fee, customers can go to a Walmart in their home country, deposit cash, and the recipient in the foreign country can withdraw the cash. This process is relatively fast, and there seems to be Walmart on every corner in the U.S. The drawback is that Walmart is not in every country, and the countries they are in may have limited locations. The U.S., Mexico, UK, China, Canada, South Africa, Chile, Japan, Costa Rica, and India are countries with relatively high numbers of locations. Make sure to check locations closest to your family. Fees are affordable and much lower than other methods of sending remittances.

Another type of remittance method is to use MoneyGram or Western Union. Western Union, which used to be a telegraph company, is the largest money transfer company globally and is very well known. Western Union has many locations around the world, so sending cash should be relatively easy. MoneyGram is Western Union's chief competitor. With MoneyGram, you can send money in person and online. Remittances can be sent to international MoneyGram locations, or you can send remittances directly to a foreign bank account. These two options have relatively high fees, but this can still be a viable approach with the many locations and ease of use.

One final low-tech method is a wire transfer from a bank. While the fees may be relatively high for small amounts of cash, this option may be a good one if you want to send large amounts of cash all at once (instead of smaller payments over many months). So, if you plan ahead and understand the elder's financial needs, this can be a great option.

On my blog, we recently published a detailed look at the best companies to send money to Mexico: https://www.multicultural caregiving.net/what-is-the-best-company-to-send-money-to-mexico/

Coordinating Care Across Borders

Perhaps you're not thinking about relocating your loved one—it may never be an option, or at least not now. Your immediate concern may be simply coordinating care and making sure they're well taken care of, and finding providers and caregiving resources can be challenging enough here in the

U.S. It gets exponentially more difficult trying to coordinate care from thousands of miles away in a different country. Doing so sounds daunting, but if you apply the principles discussed earlier in the book, it is possible to find caregiving services.

The first step is to assess your loved one's level of care needs and develop their care plan. I suggest speaking to the elder's physician or health care provider to get a clear picture of any current health conditions, severity, and medications. Be aware that some countries may have more lenient or stringent rules about sharing confidential patient data with others. Establish a relationship with their local doctor and ask about limits to these permissions. Hopefully, the provider or their staff speak English, or you speak the country's language. Despite my fluency in Spanish, I know I can easily get tripped up with some medical terminology. If communication is a concern, hiring a U.S.-based, certified medical interpreter is an option, at least for your initial investigation. Some medical offices can also offer you recommendations for senior services and resources in the area. Many countries also have the equivalent to the Area Agencies on Aging in the U.S.

Ask about governmental resources and programs as well as home-and community-based services (HCBS). There may be some entitlements that come with older age in that country. Once you have this information, perform internet searches to learn more about these foreign resources. This process will be similar to when you look for nursing homes, or other HCBS in the U.S. discussed in Chapter 4. Once you are more familiar with the available resources, you can narrow your search.

Consider hiring an established company in HCBS to help coordinate care for your loved one, someone who is the equivalent of the geriatric care managers (GCMs) or 'aging life care' managers available here in the U.S. This person will act as your local advocate and should know the health care system well. Having a local GCM coordinating care in a foreign system I don't understand is money well spent. These services abroad may be more affordable than in the U.S. This team member will save you time and help you navigate the system more efficiently. If this expense is cost-prohibitive, alternatively, you can find a trusted cousin, aunt, or another person to visit sites or collect paperwork on your behalf. Be prepared to make at least one yearly visit to ensure the resources you have in place are operationalized to your liking and have a positive effect on your loved one's well-being. Getting input from the senior by phone or WhatsApp may not reveal everything. Seniors may be reluctant to worry you and may keep important details from you. Or, if they've experienced any degree of cognitive decline, they may genuinely not perceive any dangers.

Once you have a list of resources or potential providers, it is time to put in the work to learn about the available options in the market. Look at each website, speak to your local "GCM," or trusted relative, and speak to the caregiving recipient. Then, you can request your GCM to begin the interview process for HCBS services. If the company has an office, it would be good to visit the office or facilities during one of your visits. Speak to the staff, look around, and ask a lot of questions. When you, as a caregiver or care recipient, are satisfied, it is okay to proceed.

When to Move Seniors Closer

Circumstances may change over time, and your goal may be to move your loved one (parents especially) closer to you. You may already know that if you are a U.S. Citizen, you can petition to bring your parents to live as permanent residents to the U.S. Their names must be listed on your birth certificate. There are some additional requirements for fathers, if you were born out of wedlock, if your parents are divorced, or you are adopted. As a resident of a foreign country, the elder may have to go through their government's immigration and visa process to live in the U.S legally.

Governments across the world are tightening immigration controls, and the process can be a lengthy one. It is highly recommended that you explore the process in their country early on, even if making the move is just a remote possibility. When you can start the process early, you will at least know what documentation may be lacking and begin collecting what's needed if your family decides a move is needed.

So, what might prompt you and your family to have a change of heart and consider the big move? There are several red flags to look out for and key indications that it may be time to consider moving a senior closer to you:

1. Declining Mobility

The senior is beginning to see the effects of various diseases hamper their mobility. Conditions such as arthritis, osteoporosis, foot problems due to diabetes, gout, or partial paralysis after a stroke can indicate that a senior is losing their ability to live an independent life. Other obvious signs could be a physician recommending the use of a walker or a cane and the need to hire someone to help with ADLs and IADLs. In one example, a caregiver first realized that their loved one needed help when they hadn't refilled their prescription medication in months. It turned out that the senior no longer felt comfortable taking public transportation to the pharmacy and having to beat the chaotic traffic in their country after having fallen out of the bus while trying to get on.

2. Multiple Comorbidities

While having one serious disease can be a challenge to manage, having multiple systemic diseases puts the elders at increased risk. Closer monitoring is required, more HCBS may be needed, and the costs will increase. Staying in touch with the senior's provider can alert you to developing conditions. Ask for copies of visit notes or medical records at least twice a year, more frequently if they already have other conditions you are monitoring.

3. Neurological decline

Dementia, Alzheimer's disease, Parkinson's, and even Lou Gehrig's disease dramatically affect an elder's cognitive and muscular functioning. This puts them at increased risk for car accidents, wandering, and falls. Careful and daily observations may be needed in these situations. Or, like my father's DMV incident because of his dementia, drastic action may need to be taken. Caregivers often raise concerns after visiting a relative who can no longer or is afraid to cook for themselves. They may forget to shut off the stove or find they are burning food far too often. Getting seniors a timer or other tools to help them remember may work in the short term, but this may not even be an option for more advanced cases.

4. Limited Financial Resources

Elders living abroad with limited financial resources will have fewer choices in the type of care they receive, and their standard of living may be low. With declining financial resources, you as a family member may have to help more with finances. It may get to where it costs you an incredible amount to have around-the-clock caretakers care for your parents in their home abroad. And perhaps the alternative of a senior assistive living facility in their country is as costly as in the U.S. It's important to note that seniors may become more susceptible to financial exploitation by the surrounding people, especially when coupled with declining mental or neurological health. It's a known fact that 60% of elder abuse is perpetrated by known family and friends, including caregivers (NCOA, 2020).

5. Increased Societal Risk in Home Country

Over the last year, we have seen a decline in society and increased conflicts around the world. Whether those are protests that turn violent, cartel activity, or other violence, they are worth closely monitoring the situations in your elder's home country. Unlike the U.S., some developing countries, in particular, lack a strong judicial infrastructure or social system to help those in need, and your elder may be at increased risk. Some countries may also be vulnerable to environmental and weather-related disasters. My mom's family was uprooted because of a hurricane in Quintana Roo, Mexico. For my own family, multiple events led us to altogether avoid visits south of the border. My sister and friends were visiting TJ (Tijuana) across the border when they were harassed and bullied by cops to giving a *mordida* (a bribe) to be set free over no offense at all. My father also stopped going across the border when a restaurant was shot up while getting a haircut at the barber next door.

International Relocation

Remember how much effort and time it was to move out of your last apartment or home? All the packing, cleaning, renting a truck, and driving across the state or even the country. Now imagine doing that across the world with the increased transportation fees, duties, and insurance that may be needed. Throw in the fact that this is most likely your first international move, and you are not familiar with the process. Start the planning process early so that when it is time to move, you can quickly take action to move your loved one closer to you.

The first step to planning an international move is to budget the cost of the move. Part of the costs of moving come from the distance. The further you have to move, the more it will cost due to the added transportation fees. Another factor affecting the cost is the time of year. Some months cost more than others to move in, and even the day of the week can affect the cost. Generally, the most expensive months to move in are the summer and on the weekends–which makes perfect sense because summer and the weekends are when most people will have more time. And in the summer, the weather is better with no rain or other precipitation.

Another factor affecting the cost of your move is the size and weight of your shipment. If it takes more effort to move, it's going to cost you more. Then, you select the type of transport, with air being the most expensive and sea freight the least expensive option (but slower). Please spend time coaching the senior on a strategy to select only their most precious valuables, including photos and heirlooms. It's just not worth it to ship any furniture.

Other fees and costs are also part of the moving process. Insurance is one of those costs, and in the U.S., international companies are required to offer it. Purchasing insurance may be a good idea, as the insurance can cover the total value of your cargo or reduce the amount of money the company would have to pay you back for any property damage. The final type of charge you may encounter is the customs duty charges. You will have to check each country's policy on this, but most countries do not charge fees for personal items.

Other fees for vehicle shipping and even a pet will require additional money to move. Pets may require vaccines, a pet passport, micro-chipping, and purchasing an International Air Transport Association (IATA) approved crate. And don't forget the airline ticket! Depending on location and time of year, the airline ticket cost can vary greatly. If you know when the move will be and purchase the ticket ahead of time, it will be cheaper to purchase. That assumes that you're confident you'll meet other deadlines, such as selling their home, buying insurance, cleaning out local bank accounts, and handling all other immigration requirement by your ticket date. On the flip side, a flexible ticket may be more expensive, but appropriate if certain matters don't have a clear dead. On just a cross-country move, my in-laws found themselves having to stay in a hotel for a few days, given that events didn't align perfectly. But they were prepared for this.

Traveling by airplane can be uncomfortable for seniors with mobility issues or certain health conditions. Consider bringing a neck pillow or seatbelt extender to make them more comfortable. Sleep masks and compression socks may also be helpful. You can also call the airline in advance and ensure they provide a wheelchair if needed. If they are traveling alone, the airline may be accommodating with ensuring they transfer at the right locations and be more attentive in flight. Have them carry a card with your name, address, and phone number. Be sure to walk your parent through their day of travel and what to expect and avoid going off schedule. Offer them choices where they exist. For example, do they prefer a flight with one layover or a long flight to get to their destination faster? If they experience any form of incontinence, you want to be ready with backup supplies.

We have a detailed article on the Kapok website, providing tips for traveling with seniors *(https://www. multiculturalcaregiving.net/5-important-tips-for-traveling-with-the-elderly/)* **and helpful aids** *(https://www.multiculturalcaregiving. net/adaptive-aids-for-traveling-with-seniors/).*

Once you have prepared a budget and know you can afford the move, begin the application process to immigrate or obtain legal residency in the U.S. It's best to speak to an immigration attorney as they will have experience navigating the system and help you with moving resources. Obtaining legal residency for an elder will be key to their retirement in the U.S.

Elders and caregivers should also know the challenges of moving to a new country. While the magazines and websites tout all the positives of moving to another country, there is a host of adjustments to living in a new environment and culture. Weather and climate patterns may differ from what elders are used to and may take some time to adjust. Depending on where the relocation happens, the climate can be more humid or have more precipitation than they experienced previously. During a visit last year, my father-in-law was enjoying the sun outside, but we live on the outskirts of Phoenix, the hottest place in the country. He stayed out so long that he was on the verge of a heat stroke!

If you are leaving your home country, you are also most likely leaving the social network you have built up over the years behind, as well as familiar cultural norms. Friends, family, activity partners, and even religious associations will most likely be left behind. Leaving your social network also means leaving all the activities you loved to take part as a group with; going to church or temple in your native language and seeing old friends regularly may be gone now. Gone also would be the emotional boost you get from being socially active and integrated into a network of like-minded people.

But these social attachments can be maintained if the elder is tech-savvy enough to use technology to be socially connected. As discussed earlier, apps like FaceTime and WhatsApp can be a senior's social lifeline once they have moved away to another location, including for phone calls. Taking some time to teach your loved ones the basics of technology can do wonders for their social life. But the senior must be willing to learn. Using technology is not the same as in-person social interactions, but it can help minimize social isolation.

International caregiving has its own set of challenges which the caregiver and recipient need to handle. Sending remittances, navigating the immigration system, arranging moving services, and coordinating care are some issues an international caregiver has to deal with; however, at some point, moving the senior or loved one to the U.S. may be necessary. While challenging, moving isn't entirely impossible with proper planning.

Chapter 9

Preparing for a Crisis

Planning for an elder's care should be a part of every caregiving plan. A good eldercare plan contains essential information needed to provide adequate care to the elder, even in your absence. Documenting information such as health history, medications, unique treatments required, and elder preferences provides a sound basis for the elder's healthcare team to have centralized information that their formal and informal team can reference. Without this type of plan, you may waste valuable time looking for this information; or others standing in for you may end up putting out fires as they run around trying to figure things out. Being unprepared can have severe consequences in a medical emergency when minutes and even seconds can make the difference between life and death--having documentation of your elders' caregiving needs and regimen, the likelihood that they will be well taken care of increases.

Setting and Documenting Goals

Without a plan, many care team members end up not fulfilling the needs and wishes of the elder(s) they care for and wander aimlessly. A comprehensive plan may include checklists, plans for different medical emergencies, and the legal documents necessary to carry out the wishes of the elder. One of the most important parts of the plan is where you've spelled out the explicit goals of the senior and the caregiving team. If the elder's home burned down tomorrow, would it be clear as day as to where they could go?

Goals have three essential parts to them. The first part is the goal must be **specific.** Having a goal such as, "I want to live independently and retire in a warm climate near my family and friends," is infinitely better than "I want to be happy during retirement." The former has more specific details, while the latter is too general to be of any use. Another goal can be "I want to live in a one-level home and have a yard where I can continue gardening."

Next, the goal must be **realistic** and **achievable**. Finding a home within one's budget near their family and friends is very realistic and achievable. Retiring in a mansion while receiving $1,000/month from Social Security is *not* realistic and *not* achievable.

The goal must be *measurable.* You must be able to document and measure the results to be attained. Finding one home within one's budget of $1,000 in the same city as the elder's children is a measurable metric. However, one may debate over whether it is actually achievable, especially if the average rental is over $2,000/month.

Finally, the goal must be **timely.** There must be a deadline or timeframe for the goals to be achieved or at least actions taken. While there may be delays and unexpected errors, at least the deadline can give the team a sense of urgency to continue progressing. A deadline should be created so that things continue to move forward.

So, it's time for the interview with the elder. Remember to document it as this will be the beginning of the eldercare plan. If a caregiver needs help to organize eldercare services to create a plan, formal team members such as GCMs (geriatric care managers) may be something to look into a little more. Think of GCMs as hubs in their field. They can plan what is needed and work for the elder. This can be a money-saving decision as the GCM should put the elder's best interest in mind and only recommend needed services. Without a GCM on your side, a caregiver (especially an inexperienced one) is subject to some costly mistakes.

Delivering Eldercare Services

After interviewing your loved one to understand their unique situation better and creating goals to assist them with delivering their care, now it's time to help put plans in place. To do this effectively, you'll need to organize the legal steps and work on other logistics.

The elder's information should be organized in a manner that is accessible to other caregivers when needed. Establishing a good working or friendly relationship with other would-be partners in care is crucial because exchanging this very personal information could be perceived as very intrusive. Trust and open communication are vital–the key is to begin and establish these things before they are needed.

Basic information like an elder's contact information, next of kin, insurance information, and financial accounts will be required. Other more personal information like income, health history, medications, current treatments, and wills are equally vital to the delivery of caregiving and will also be needed.

Below is a list of information that you will need to gather as part of the caregiving plan. The key is to document them and have them accessible to caregiving team members. Having a binder or folder with hard copies of this information and digital copies on a USB drive is highly recommended.

Health, Financial and Personal Information that Caregivers Should Document

Personal Information	Health Insurance
<ul><li>Legal name</li><li>Date of birth</li><li>Address</li><li>Phone number</li><li>Email address (optional)</li><li>Next of kin (and their contact information)</li><li>Social Security number</li><li>Medicare number</li><li>Driver's license number and state issued</li></ul>	<ul><li>Health insurance company name</li><li>Health insurance benefits card<ul><li>Medical</li><li>Dental</li><li>Prescription</li><li>Vision</li></ul></li><li>Health insurance benefits contract</li><li>Services provided</li><li>Deductibles</li></ul>
Health Care Professionals	Financial Information
<ul><li>Primary care physician</li><li>Specialists</li></ul>	<ul><li>Checking/savings account</li><li>Health Savings Account</li></ul>

• Dental • Optometry • Contact information for each provider	• Credit card/ checks • Billing address information
Health History	**Medications**
• Current diseases • Previous diseases • Surgeries • Prior falls	• Current medications and dosage • Recent past • Scheduling system
Nutrition	**Transportation**
• Vitamins • Supplements • Special dietary requirements	• Special requirements • Mobility aids • Driver information • Public bus schedule / common routes
Legal Information	
• Health proxy • Living wills • Power of Attorney	

Looking at the table above, you can see how personal all of this information is. You are basically in all parts of a senior's life. Therefore, establishing trust and communicating are such important parts of the caregiving process.

Plan for Emergencies

Now, you should have the senior's goals in place and all of their information organized and accessible. Next, plan for the expected emergencies. Knowing where to go and who to call promptly is crucial in these emergencies. Minutes and even seconds can be the difference between life and death.

Money can also be saved when care is appropriately coordinated. Trips to the emergency room, surgeries, urgent care, or even a call to the ambulance can cost thousands more than necessary if the medical insurance policy is not understood. My family and I learned this the hard way as well. When we recently moved to Arizona, we didn't take the time to familiarize ourselves with the surrounding medical facilities. When my daughter ran a high fever, we inadvertently went to the most expensive ER that overcharged us in every way possible. Soon enough, we learned that the nursing staff on our insurance company's twenty-four-hour line were better able to direct us to qualified urgent cares in their network. With some prior planning, you save out-of-pocket costs incurred by the elder's health insurance benefits. Why go to the emergency room when a visit to urgent care can be as effective and cheaper? Reviewing the health insurance policy will be key to understanding the most efficient course of action. For example, many pharmacy insurance companies provide significant discounts for signing up for mail-order medication.

One emergency that may come up is allergic reactions (i.e., anaphylactic shock). Does the caregiving team (this can include family members and anyone involved in daily care activities) know about the signs for these types of emergencies? Are they aware if they have an allergy to penicillin or anything else? Do they have the necessary supplies, like an epinephrine pen or, with mild allergies, an antihistamine? Other medications and supplies could be a basic first aid kit, incontinence supplies, and even alcohol swabs. These are essential supplies to keep in a handy bag.

Dementia is a common medical condition for seniors. Like my father and his adventure across the Mexican border, seniors often wander off on their own if not carefully monitored. It was fortunate that my sister's strategic placement of a GPS tracker in his car allowed us to track him easily. Do you have security measures on the house to prevent wandering? Is the nursing home the seniors are staying at specially trained and equipped to keep dementia patients from wandering off?

Another emergency could be a heart attack or stroke. Knowing the symptoms is key to understanding how to respond. While we do not provide medical advice, make sure to speak to a legally licensed health professional for an official diagnosis of any health condition. There are symptoms to be on the lookout for, such as tightness in the chest or arms, nausea, shortness of breath, fatigue, and lightheadedness. In this situation, call 911 or someone to take you to the hospital immediately. If you were prescribed nitroglycerin tablets, now may be a good time to take one as you wait for help to arrive. If you see someone passed out from a heart attack, call 911 and begin CPR while you wait for the ambulance to come. Having this advanced training will help you stay calm and confident should you find yourself in this situation.

Another common type of emergency is diabetes-related emergencies. Hypoglycemia (low blood sugar) and hyperglycemia (high blood sugar) can quickly lead to critical situations. Hypoglycemia happens when blood sugar levels fall below 70 mg/dl and are usually insulin. Symptoms of hypoglycemia include confusion, dizziness, and nausea.

Chills, shaking, weakness, and even loss of consciousness can occur. To resolve this issue, the hypoglycemic person can take something high in carbohydrates or sugar, such as juice, candy, and a glucose tablet. This should give relief quickly. If not, it's best to see your physician or call 911. We talked about having supplies on hand, and when it comes to diabetes, that's one area where being short on supplies can be a matter of life or death. With my daughter's type 1 diabetes, we've become accustomed to always having a 'diabetes' bag handy that includes glucose tabs, her glucose monitor, test strips, and more as a backup. We would be the most irresponsible parents to be out and about with her without a Glucagon pen. It takes just a little exercise at the playground to see her blood glucose quickly plummet.

Hyperglycemia is the opposite of hypoglycemia: high blood sugar. Symptoms of hyperglycemia include excessive thirst, frequent urination, headaches, and blurry vision. To reduce the effects of hyperglycemia, you can exercise to burn off excess sugars, eat less, or speak to your physician about the dose of insulin you are taking. Persistently elevated blood sugar levels can lead to other life-threatening conditions and should be attended to as soon as possible.

While not immediately life-threatening, incontinence can appear to be an emergency, especially for the person experiencing it. Incontinence, if you are not familiar with the term, refers to urinary or bowel-based issues. There are various types of urinary incontinence that a caregiver or elder may want to be prepared for; the first type of incontinence is functional incontinence. This type of incontinence affects older adults because it has more to do with an elder's mobility. Difficulties with mobility mean that the elder may not be able to move fast enough to the restroom on time. The second type of incontinence is urge incontinence, where the senior suddenly feels the need to urinate but cannot hold the urine long enough to make it to the restroom. The third type of incontinence is overflow incontinence. This is where the bladder does not empty completely, and small amounts of urine will leak. Various medical conditions, such as spinal cord injuries, diabetes, and enlarged prostates, can cause this type of incontinence. The last type of incontinence is stress incontinence, where urine will leak from the bladder when pressure is placed on it. The pressure or stress can be the result of laughing, sneezing, or exercising.

Products such as incontinence bed protectors, a raised toilet, and incontinence underwear, as well as Kegel exercises, can help minimize the emergencies at home or in public associated with incontinence. I am proud to say that we have written various articles on the Kapok website about this subject. You can visit the links below for more information about incontinence:

https://www.multiculturalcaregiving.net/tackling-urinary-incontinence-in-seniors-respectively/

https://www.multiculturalcaregiving.net/managing-incontinence-in-dementia-patients/

While it is best to discuss with your physician the best course of action to take in these medical situations, the key is being prepared and having an action plan to know what to do immediately. Of course, having all the elder's information centralized in a convenient location helps in case a dash to the emergency room is needed.

The Impact of COVID-19

The COVID-19 pandemic is the prime example of the type of emergency one didn't see coming. Many caregivers were unprepared. They had no stand-in for them should they become ill or hospitalized, and others had no reserve of supplies at home as swarms of people cleaned out the shelves at their local grocery stores.

The pandemic seemed to hit everyone by surprise, and our leadership was slow to respond. It was left up to individuals to take precautions and prepare for lockdown. If you were among 'the prepared' and were diligent in your emergency planning when this black swan occurred, you were probably at home breathing a sigh of relief. As everyone else was scrambling about, you likely had adequate medical supplies, enough food (special dietary requirements are fundamental), and water stored. You knew who to reach out to for relevant advice and information. You had a list of alternative facilities to take the elder or yourself if your preferred hospital was overloaded. If not prepared, you were waiting hours in line to purchase necessities (if you could find them) and without essential medical supplies like insulin or epi-pens.

Few alive today had ever experienced lockdown and stay-in-place orders, and unprepared people were caught off guard. Businesses were doing their best to implement new policies. This left my mom in a pickle as she tried to handle her banking. Her bank only permitted one person at a time. However, she knew she couldn't leave my dad, who has advanced Alzheimer's, in the car or even outside, knowing he could wander off. She tried to explain this to the overwhelmed bank staff at the door, but they didn't grasp the situation well and shooed her away. After that, my mother struggled to run the most basic of errands because, on most outings, she had to wrestle with my dad to keep his mask on. This further isolated her, and she had to resort often to asking favors from family and friends.

While we continue to learn additional facts about the virus, what is certain is that seniors were disproportionately dying from its complications. Approximately 80% of deaths were from those sixty-five and older. Racial/minority groups, including African-American, Latino, and Native American, were especially hard-hit (Centers for Disease Control 'COVID Data Tracker'). Patients with certain underlying medical conditions such as cancer, chronic kidney disease, heart conditions, chronic obstructive pulmonary disease (COPD), diabetes, and severe obesity were at increased risk of severe illness and death from the virus.

Another unintended result of the pandemic's lockdowns is social isolation. While short-term isolation can be tolerated for a while, this degree of persistent social isolation has long-term negative effects on mental health. Faster cognitive decline, poor diets, and higher disease rates can result from loneliness resulting from social isolation. Other symptoms and conditions of social isolation include depression, anxiety, post-traumatic stress, and substance abuse.

Experts in the field of aging had already recognized social isolation as a major health problem in seniors that became even more prominent in the age of COVID-19. Taking part in physical exercise, volunteering, taking a class, and changing living conditions can help reduce or prevent the negative symptoms of loneliness. To learn more about social isolation in seniors, you can visit the Kapok website through the link below:

https://www.multiculturalcaregiving.net/loneliness-and-isolation-in-seniors-an-infographic-guide/

Social participation and having a support network have been shown as suitable protective measures for maintaining good mental health. As a caregiver or an elder, you should maintain your own relationships and stay mentally healthy. During this time of social distancing, caregivers can use technology to maintain relationships with their seniors and help seniors maintain their own relationships. Staying connected to others is the key to sustaining your mental health. You can read more about the use of technology to combat loneliness for elders on the Kapok website by visiting the links below:

https://www.multiculturalcaregiving.net/social-isolation-older-adults-technology/

https://www.multiculturalcaregiving.net/best-social-apps-for-seniors/

Planning for Eldercare in the Age of COVID-19

As of this writing, about 50% of the U.S. population has been fully vaccinated. While still far from herd immunity, we are rounding the corner. The COVID-19 virus and its potentially dangerous variants remain a threat to unvaccinated populations, and we now have our guard up. The next pandemic is less likely to take us by surprise.

Caring for the Caregiver

One irony of eldercare is that caregivers, the ones who primarily care for elders, are often found to become sick themselves. And now, with the risk of COVID-19, caregivers may be at greater risk because of additional stress and social isolation. Caregivers should expect emotional and physical burnout unless preventive measures are taken. Instead of waiting for signs to appear, proactive measures may be a good idea. If not for the physical and mental health of the caregiver, then for the sake of the elder.

Many caregivers must balance work and family life with their caregiving services. Nearly half of caregivers say it's "moderately to complicated to balance work and caregiving." Even with the difficulties of caregiving, 90% of all caregivers say that it is a worthwhile endeavor (Swanson and Alonso-Zaldivar, 2017).

Respite care is a service provided to elders so that their primary caregivers can take a break (or "respite") from their everyday routine. With the extra responsibilities of caregiving and the physical, emotional, and spiritual toll it takes on the caregiver, only 15% receive any type of respite care. It is no wonder then that many caregivers experience depression at some point. One study found that 23% of surveyed caregivers experienced either moderate or severe depression (Bach, 2017), and for dementia caregivers, that number is even higher at 34% (Sallim, Sayampanathan, and Cuttilan, 2015). The number of caregivers experiencing depressive symptoms without a formal diagnosis maybe even higher. Having a break is a necessary long-term strategy to give caregivers a chance to recharge and rest. Taking one week off once or twice a year can do wonders for helping the caregiver recharge and prevent burnout.

Therefore, planning respite care into the care plan should be a preventive activity that helps maintain emotional and physical energy for when it is needed most. How can a caregiver take care of someone to the best of their ability if they are deprived of adequate sleep? Or how will a caregiver lift carry grocery bags if their muscles are weak or achy? The answer to these rhetorical questions: they can't.

Like most medical conditions, there are symptoms related to burnout that caregivers and the caregiving team should know. Some of the early warning signs of caregiver burnout are remarkably similar to depression (Cleveland Clinic): emotional and physical exhaustion, social withdrawal, loss of interest in enjoyable activities, changes in weight or appetite, sleep disturbances, feelings of helplessness, excessive use of intoxicants, and difficulty concentrating. If you have these symptoms, it may be time to see your physician or schedule some respite care.

The best way to be aware of impending burnout is to be self-aware and monitor your emotions and physical well-being. How do you feel towards the elder you are taking care of? Do you feel resentment, guilt, or a burden? Are you verbally abusing your elder and often feeling enraged? Has your lifestyle changed since you began caregiving? Are you overeating or eating a lot of "comfort food?" Are you exercising less these days? Is your performance at work slipping? Are you sleep-deprived? Do you find yourself crying and not laughing? Are you drinking or doing drugs more often? Are you having sleep issues?

Often, caregivers will neglect their own self-care, so it is important to get adequate sleep, eat a healthy diet, and exercise regularly. It would be best if you were doing these self-care activities anyway, but sometimes a friendly reminder doesn't hurt. The consequence of not taking care of yourself is that the quality of your care goes down. So, take care of yourself so you can take care of your elder. Do you ever wonder why you are advised to give yourself oxygen first in an airplane during an emergency? This advice is given even if you have a loved one or a child next to you. The answer is: for the caregiver to give care, they must take care of themselves first. How will you help your child during an emergency if you are on the ground passed out?

Treating Caregiver Burnout

So, what should you do if you feel burnout symptoms coming on? First, one option is to get professional help. See your primary care physician, psychiatrist, or licensed therapist and get help. Have someone who has already been medically trained to evaluate your condition.

Simply having a friend to share your experiences with can be cathartic and feel therapeutic. A therapist can also give you coping and relaxation strategies to deal with the pressures of caregiving. Seek treatment (if necessary) for yourself or think of the elder you are caring for and do it for them (most likely, they are a loved one in the family).

Another way you can ask for help is through your social network, whether it be your family or friends. The people in your network may have had experience with the same symptoms or know someone who has the same symptoms. You can seek out other caregivers to ask for their advice and support. Speaking to others with shared experiences can help with elder problems and provide emotional support to a stressful experience. Remember that over one in every five Americans acts as a caregiver (AARP and National Alliance for Caregiving, 2020). You're not alone. Reach out.

Many online caregiver support and social groups meet in person or online, and there are many online forums available today to help support caregivers and elders through this journey. There are also many general forums or disease-specific forums that you may join. AgingCare forum hosts excellent threads for caregivers *(https://www.agingcare.com/ caregiver-forum)*, the Alzheimer's Association hosts the *https:// www.alzconnected.org/*, and you can search for Facebook groups too.

Another option if you feel the effects of burnout is to take a break. Respite care services referenced in this book can help make this happen. You can also enlist the help of close family and friends. Some may have been looking for ways to help you – now, you can take them up on the offer. It doesn't mean that you're moving to Tahiti, but a weekend away or two will help you reset. Taking time away from the elder and the stresses related to it should help you recover.

Besides time off, continuing other self-care activities should help your physical, mental, and emotional health improve. Hopefully, this time away from the elder and the strain of performing caregiving services will help you recover your physical, mental, and emotional well-being. Only from this position of health can you give the service your loved one deserves. Time away from the elder has another benefit–the elder may need a break from you! Yes, too much time spent with one person (as much as you love them) can negatively affect both parties.

Planning for the Final Phase of Life

Is there an end in sight to your caregiving role? There is. Either someone else takes your place or your loved one passes. Death is never a comfortable subject to talk about, but it is an important and necessary one. The last days in anyone's life is a process that merits careful discussion and review so that it is as clear as day what the elder wants to have done during their process and when they are gone. What are their medical treatment wishes near the end of life? Where do they want to live? How do they want to say their goodbyes? Where do they want to be buried? Do they want to be buried? What are you going to do with their estate? For a moment, consider this question yourself: What does a good death look like for you?

As the elder gets nearer to the end of life and begin their process of dealing with death, they can sense when they will pass and begin verbalizing cryptic messages. They bargain with God for a little more time to achieve some goal (i.e., see their grandchild get married). Statements like, "I hope to see you at Christmas next year, God willing," may be signs that the elder thinks the end is near. This may be an excellent time to start the discussion if you have not already started it yet.

The process of dying can take different forms for different people. Some will pass away quickly, and some will go through a multi-year process. We often assume that everyone is as scared of death as you may be now. It is not uncommon for terminally ill and other persons close to death to experience seeing deceased family members in their dreams or at their bedside, providing a sense of comfort and peace to the dying. Look to your shared beliefs to come to terms with death. Being in this field, I can more freely talk with others about the final stages and even the afterlife. My young daughter already understands mortality to some degree. We don't live forever, but that's what makes life richer and what makes our relationships to others even more valuable. What's more, for all we know, there's something grander for us on the other side.

The dying process is just as diverse and unique as to how this person lived their life, so no two situations are identical. Another aspect of this process is end-of-life comfort. Depending on the elder's condition, the caregiver has options. One widespread comfort option is hospice and palliative care–specialists in end-of-life comfort. Hospice care differs from other types of medical treatment in that the goal is not to cure but to provide support and comfort to an elder's remaining life. By attending to the patient's emotional and spiritual needs, hospice and palliative care focus on relieving pain and symptoms. They. Healthcare professionals (i.e., doctors, pharmacists, nurses, aides, and spiritual counselors) are specially trained to administer hospice care to provide the needed comfort. Unfortunately, many minority communities hold negative stereotypes about hospice that lead them to forego these wonderful services (Johnson & Wellman, 2020). If you or your loved one are among them, I highly urge you to be open-minded and receptive. Don't let your assumptions deprive your loved one of this comfort care.

The Final Plan

Eventually, death visits us all, and what the elder decides to do with their remains will determine your course of action. The key is to have this difficult conversation first and have a plan for this eventuality. Having a plan in place, especially if the elder creates it themselves, can help to fulfill all of their needs and desires of the final event in their life. The key to this result is planning ahead.

The ins and outs of planning and paying for the funeral may be unique. The first step is to determine where they want their remains to be laid to rest. If it is a cemetery, the cemetery's location and location of the plot within the cemetery can determine the price. Some people want to be laid to rest next to family members, and others may want to be buried in their country of birth.

After deciding on the location, I suggest visiting some of the cemetery locations in this geographical area. Then, you can speak to the funeral directors there. The funeral director and the staff are generally on call and can help you decide between options and help coordinate other services for you.

Other factors to consider when funeral planning is transportation (of the deceased from home or medical facility to the funeral home), transportation of loved ones (in a hearse) during the funeral procession, venue selection, casket, and cremation containers, burial vaults, third party services, and other miscellaneous services.

There are many options for different price points and will depend on how much the elder wants to spend on their funeral. The options exist to meet many budgets, from simple cremations to high-end options (private cemeteries with elaborate decorations). And if you want to be at the cutting edge of funeral services, newer burial options, such as "alkaline hydrolysis" (flameless cremation) and "green burials" may be available in your area. Remember to plan ahead and use the funeral directors and their staff as your points of contact.

One last note is to make sure to report the deceased person's death to Social Security. Any benefits received during the month of death must be returned to Social Security, and any checks sent to the deceased must remain uncashed and returned to Social Security. Spouses may receive a onetime payment of $255 from Social Security, and others may be eligible for the monthly payments if they meet certain conditions.

Some of the family members that may be eligible for the monthly benefit may be:

◊ Widow or widower aged over sixty years old (over fifty, if disabled)

◊ Widow or widower caring for a deceased child who is under sixteen years

◊ An unmarried child of the deceased

◊ Under eighteen years old (nineteen if a full-time student in elementary or secondary school)

◊ Age eighteen or older with a disability before age twenty-two

◊ Certain grandchildren/stepchildren under certain circumstances

◊ Parents aged over sixty-two years old

◊ Surviving divorced spouse (under certain circumstances)

A good caregiving plan will have many parts to it. Documenting goals, gathering all relevant information, and planning for the eventual emergencies should be included in the caregiving plan. Planning respite care and breaks for the caregiver will also help maintain the quality of services by preventing caregiver burnout. The final phase of life and eventual death of the elder, while not a welcomed topic to many, should also be included as the final plan in this senior's life.

As the person who has likely spent the most time with your loved one, it will take a tremendous toll on your emotional and physical health when they pass away. You're entitled to and deserve the space to grieve, but I implore you to reach out to others for emotional support and help, just as you might do during any period that you experience burnout. Avoid blaming yourself for anything that may have occurred in your loved one's final days. Caregivers are tremendously hard on themselves despite the enormous self-sacrifice they've given to care for their loved one in helping them lead a dignified life through declining health and disability. My hope is that, through this book, you have taken away an array of tools, resources, and understanding of the incredible role you play in our aging society. Across this country and around the world, caregivers like you are figuring it out, one day at a time.

About the Author

Angelica P. Herrera-Venson, DrPH, MPH was born in San Diego, CA and lived in Mexico for the first seven years of her life. With a lifelong interest in gerontology and personal experience with the challenges of caregiving and eldercare, she earned a Doctorate in Public Health and pursued opportunities to research the social determinants of healthy aging among minority and immigrant communities. In her current role, she supports community health centers' transition into Medicaid value-based to deliver high quality, cost-effective healthcare that improves their health outcomes. At the National Council on Aging, Angelica managed the nation's largest database of chronic disease self-management and aging programs.

Angelica has written a multitude of peer-reviewed publications on the sociocultural influences of Hispanic/Latino families' use of long-term services and support, disparities in diabetes treatment, and the epidemiology of depression in racial-ethnic minority populations. Before joining the faculty at the University of Maryland, Baltimore County, she completed several research fellowships and training for her work in the public health and aging sector: Post-Doctoral Fellow at the National Institute of Mental Health in the Advanced Center for Innovation in Services and Intervention Research (2008-2009), Kellogg Health Scholar (2009-2010), recipient of the *Kaiser Burch Minority Leadership Award* (2012-2013), and a Health and Aging Policy Fellow (2010-2011).

In 2014, Angelica founded her website *(https://www. multiculturalcaregiving.net/)* to provide resources and guidance about the challenges of aging and caregiving in a multicultural modern environment. On this website, readers will find advice for managing the many aspects of caregiving, aging well, managing finances while caring for others, finding housing and public benefits, as well as food and nutrition. There is a growing archive of articles in Spanish. As a result of witnessing her family's struggle with health and social services, Angelica attained formal academic training in aging and developed Kapok Aging and Caregiver Resources to simplify the journey for older adults and their caregivers. *Multicultural Guide to Caregiving* is her first book and the culmination of many years of research.

Angelica now lives in Chandler, Arizona with her husband and her daughter, Lola. When she is not researching ways to improve the lives of racial-ethnic minorities, you can find Angelica exploring the great outdoors with her family and soaking up the local culture.

Website: *https://www.multiculturalcaregiving.net/*
Email: *yaxche9@gmail.com*

Glossary of Terms

AAA – Area Agency on Aging

AARP – American Association of Retired Persons

Acculturation – A process of assimilation to another culture, typically the dominant one

ACL – Administration for Community Living

ADL – Activities of Daily Living

ADRC – Aging and Disability Resource Centers

ALF – Assisted Living Facility

APTA – American Public Transportation Association

CCRC – Continuous Care Retirement Community

CDC – Centre for Disease Control

CFP – Certified Financial Planner

ChFP – Chartered Financial Planner

COPD – Chronic Obstructive Pulmonary Disease

CPI – Corruption Perceptions Index

CPR – Cardiopulmonary resuscitation

CSFP – Commodity Supplemental Food Program

DES – Department of Economic Security

DNI – Do-not-intubate

DNR – Do-not-resuscitate

DrPH – Doctorate in Public Health

FAFSA – Free Application for Federal Student Aid

Familism – Putting the family's wellbeing over the interest of a single member

FRA – Full Retirement Age

FWB – Financial Well-Being

G7 – Group of Seven countries (USA, Canada, Italy, United Kingdom, Germany, France, EU)

GCM – Geriatric Care Manager

HCBS – Home and Community-Based Services

HIPAA – Health Insurance Portability and Accountability Act

HOPA – Housing for Older Persons Act

HUD – Department of Housing and Urban Development

IADL – Instrumental Activities of Daily Living

IATA – International Air Transport Association

IHSS – In-Home Supportive Services

IL – Independent Living

LIHEAP – The Low-Income Energy Assistance Program

LIS – Low-Income Subsidy

LPN – Licensed Practice Nurse

LTC – Long-Term Care

LVN – Licensed Vocational Nurse

LW – Living Will

MPA – Medical Power of Attorney

MSP – Medicare Savings Program

NORC – Naturally Occurring Retirement Community

OAA – Older Americans Act

PAP – Patient Assistance Program

PHA – Public Housing Authority

QDWI – Qualified Disabled and Working Individuals

QLI – Qualified Individual

QMB – Qualified Medicare Beneficiary

Remittance – A transfer of money over international borders

RN – Registered Nurse

SFMNP – Senior Farmer's Market Nutrition Program

SLMB – Specified Low-Income Medicare Beneficiary

SNAP – Supplemental Nutrition Assistance Program

SNF – Skilled Nursing Facility

SPAP – State Pharmaceutical Assistance Program

SSDI – Social Security Disability Insurance

SSI – Social Security Income

TEFAP – The Emergency Food Assistance Program

TJ – Tijuana

UCSD – University of California, San Diego

USDA – United States Department of Agriculture

WAP – Weatherization Assistance Program

Works Cited

Administration for Community Living. "How Much Care Will You Need." DHHS. 2020. Web. 10 August 2021 https://acl.gov/ltc/basic-needs/how-much-care-will-you-need.

AARP and National Alliance for Caregiving. "Caregiving in the United States 2020." AARP. 2020. Web. 14 May 2020 https://www.aarp.org/ppi/info-2020/caregiving-in-the-united-states.html.

Alzheimer's Association. "2015 Alzheimer's disease facts and figures." 2015. Web. 10 August 2021. https://www.alz.org/media/Documents/2015FactsAndFigures.pdf.

AP and NORC. "Long-term care in America: Hispanics' cultural concerns and difficulties with care." The Long-Term Care Poll. Web. 10 August 2021. https://www.longtermcarepoll.org/long-term-care-in-america-hispanics-cultural-concerns-and-difficulties-with-care/

Bach, Becky. "Caregivers experience high rates of anxiety, depression, study finds". Stanford Medicine. 2017. Web. 10 August 2021. https://scopeblog.stanford.edu/2017/02/16/caregivers-experience-high-rates-of-anxiety-depression-study-finds/

Baughman, Reagan, and Smith Kirstin E, "Labor mobility of the direct care workforce: Implications for the provision of long-term care." *Health Economics* 21.12 (2012): n. pag. Research Gate. Web. 10 August 2021 https://www.researchgate.net/publication/51743495_Labor_Mobility_of_the_Direct_Care_Workforce_Implications_for_the_Provision_of_Long-Term_Care

Brown, Jennifer and Oakley Diane. "Latinos' retirement insecurity in the United States." UNIDOS US. 2018. Web. 10 August 2021.   22 January 2021 http://publications.unidosus.org/bitstream/handle/123456789/1903/latinoretirement_unidosus_nirs_report_112818_lr.pdf?sequence=4&isAllowed=y.

Brown, H Shelton, Herrera Angelica P., and Angel, Jacqueline. "Opportunity costs associated with caring for older Mexican-Americans." *Journal of Cross-Cultural Gerontology* 28.3 (2013) : 375-389. NCBI. Web. 10 August 2021. https://dx.doi.org/10.1007%2Fs10823-013-9208-3

Centers for Disease Control and Prevention. "COVID-19 Mortality Overview". National Center for Health Statistics. 2021. Web10 August 2021. https://www.cdc.gov/nchs/covid19/mortality-overview.html.

Centers for Disease Control and Prevention. "COVID Data Tracker." National Center for Health Statistics. 2021. Web. 10 August 2021. https://covid.cdc.gov/covid-data-tracker/#demographics.

Cleveland Clinic. "Caregiver burnout." 2021. Web.10 August 2021. https://my.clevelandclinic.org/health/diseases/9225-caregiver-burnout.

Crist, Janice D., et al. "Caregiving burden, acculturation, familism, and Mexican American elders' use of home care services." *Research and Theory for Nursing Practice*, 23.3 (2009): 165-180. NCBI. Web. 10 August 2021. https://www.ncbi.nlm.nih.gov/pmc/articles/PMC6467067/

Evercare and National Alliance for Caregiving. "Evercare® study of Hispanic family caregiving in the U.S." 2008. Web. 10 August

2021. https://www.caregiving.org/wp-content/uploads/2020/05/Hispanic_Caregiver_Study_web_ENG_FINAL_11_04_08.pdf.

Feng, Zhanlian, Fennell Mary L., Tyler Denise A., Clark Melissa, and Vincent Mor. "Growth of racial and ethnic minorities in US nursing homes driven by demographics and possible disparities in options." Health Affairs 30.7 (2011):1358-1365. The Care Span. Web. 10 August 2021. https://www.healthaffairs.org/doi/pdf/10.1377/hlthaff.2011.0126.

Fennell, Mary L., Feng Zhanlian, and Melissa A Clark. "Elderly Hispanics more likely to reside in poor-quality nursing homes." Health Affairs 29. 1 (2010) : 65-73. The Care Span. Web. 10 August 2021. https://www.healthaffairs.org/doi/10.1377/hlthaff.2009.0003.

Fisher, Gwenith G., et al. "Caring for individuals with dementia and cognitive impairment, not dementia: findings from the aging, demographics, and memory study." Journal of the American Geriatrics Society 59.3 (2011): 488-494. NCBI. Web. 10 August 2021. https://pubmed.ncbi.nlm.nih.gov/21391939/

Gaugler, Joseph E., Kane Robert L., Kane Rosalie, and Robert J Newcomer. "Predictors of institutionalization in Latinos with Dementia." Journal of Cross-Cultural Gerontology 21.3-4 (2006): 139-155. Web. 10 August 2021. https://doi.org/10.1007/s10823-006-9029-8

Geanous, Jacob. "Comatose woman who gave birth was 'raped and impregnated by care worker multiple times." Metro U.K. 2019. Web. 10 August 2021. https://metro.co.uk/2019/05/23/comatose-woman-who-gave-birth-was-raped-and-impregnated-by-care-worker-multiple-times-9667582/

Herrera, Angelica P., George Rebecca, Angel Jacqueline L., Markides Kyriakos, and Torres-Gil, Fernando. "Variation in Older Americans Act caregiver service use, unmet hours of care, and independence among Hispanics, African Americans, and Whites."

Home Health Care Services Quarterly 32.1 (2013): 35-56. NCBI. Web. 10 August 2021. https://pubmed.ncbi.nlm.nih.gov/23438508/

Herrera, Angelica P., Lee Jerry, Palos Guadalupe, and Torres-Vigil Isabel. "Cultural influences in the patterns of long-term care use among Mexican American family caregivers." Journal of Applied Gerontology 27.2 (2008) : 141-165. Sage Journals. Web. 10 August 2021. https://journals.sagepub.com/doi/10.1177/0733464807310682

Houser, Ari, and Mary Jo Gibson. Valuing the Invaluable: The Economic Value of Family Caregiving, 2008 Update. US National Library of Science (2008): n.pag AARP.. Web. 10 August 2021. http://resource.nlm.nih.gov/101491762

Johnson Shen, Megan Wellman, Joseph D. "Evidence of Palliative Care Stigma: The Role of Negative Stereotypes in Preventing Willingness to Utilize Palliative Care". Palliative Support Care. 17.4 (2019): 374–380 .NCBI. Web. 10 August 2021. https://www.ncbi.nlm.nih.gov/pmc/articles/PMC6551309/

Kaye, H. Stephen, LaPlante Mitchell P., and Charlene Harrington. "Do noninstitutional long-term care services reduce Medicaid spending?" Health Affairs (Millwood). 28.1 (2009): 262-272. NCBI. Web. 10 August 2021. https://pubmed.ncbi.nlm.nih.gov/19124878/

Livingston, Gretchen. "In a down economy, fewer births" Pew Research Center. (2011): n. pag. Web. 10 August 2021. https://www.pewresearch.org/social-trends/2011/10/12/in-a-down-economy-fewer-births/

Mendes, Elizabeth. "Most Caregivers look after elderly parent; Invest a lot of time". Gallup. 2011. Web. 10 August 2021. https://news.gallup.com/poll/148682/caregivers-look-elderly-parent-invest-lot-time.aspx.

Montgomery, Rhonda J.V., Holley Lyn, Deichert Jerome, and Karl Kosloski. "A profile of home care workers from the 2000

Census: How it changes what we know." *The Gerontologist.* 45.5 (2005): 593-600. Web. 10 August 2021. https://academic.oup.com/gerontologist/article/45/5/593/652568

Mor, Vincent, Zinn Jacqueline, Angelenni Joseph, Teno Joan M., and Susan C. Miller. "Driven to tiers: Socioeconomic and racial disparities in the quality of nursing home care." *The Milbank Quarterly.* 82.2 (2004): 227-256. NCBI. Web. 10 August 2021 https://pubmed.ncbi.nlm.nih.gov/15225329/

National Alliance for Caregiving and AARP Family Caregiving. "Caregiving in the U.S.: 2020 Report". 2020. Web. 10 August 2021. https://www.aarp.org/content/dam/aarp/ppi/2020/05/full-report-caregiving-in-the-united-states.doi.10.26419-2Fppi.00103.001.pdf.

National Alliance for Caregiving and AARP Family Caregiving. "Caregiving in the U.S.: 2015 Report". 2015. Web. 10 August 2021. https://www.aarp.org/content/dam/aarp/ppi/2015/caregiving-in-the-united-states-2015-report-revised.pdf

National Council on Aging (NCOA). "Get the Facts on Elder Abuse." 2021. Web. 10 August 2021. https://www.ncoa.org.

Nguyen, Anne. "Cultural and social attitudes towards mental illness in Ho Chi Minh City, Vietnam." *Seattle University Research Journal.* 2 (2003): 27-31.

National Vital Statistics System (NVSS). "Vital statistics rapid release: Report No. 004". 2018.Web. 10 August 2021. https://www.cdc.gov/nchs/data/vsrr/report004.pdf.

Orszag, Peter R., and Rodriguez Eric. "Retirement Security for Latinos: Bolstering coverage, savings, and adequacy." 2005. Web. 10 August 2021. https://www.pewtrusts.org/-/media/legacy/uploadedfiles/phg/content_level_pages/reports/rsplaraza071305pdf.pdf.

Paz, Karen Yuridia, and Kelly Massey. "Health disparity among Latina women: Comparison with non-Latina women."

Clinical Medicine Insights Women's Health 9. 1 (2016) :71-74. Research Gate. Web. 10 August 2021. https://www.researchgate.net/publication/305486482_Health_Disparity_among_Latina_Women_Comparison_with_Non-Latina_Women

PHI National. "Caring for the Future: The Power and Potential of America's Direct Care Workforce". 2021. Web. 10 August 2021. https://phinational.org/resource/caring-for-the-future-the-power-and-potential-of-americas-direct-care-workforce/.

Reinhard, Susan C., Kassner Enid, Houser Ari, and Robert Mollica. "Raising expectations: A state scorecard on long-term services and supports for older adults, people with physical disabilities, and family caregivers." AARP. 2011. Web. 10 August 2021. https://assets.aarp.org/rgcenter/ppi/ltc/ltss_scorecard.pdf.

Reinhard, Susan, Feinberg Lynn F, Houser Ari, Choula Rita, and Evans Molly. "Valuing the Invaluable 2019 Update: Charting a Path Forward," AARP. 2019. Web. 10 August 2021. https://www.aarp.org/ppi/info-2015/valuing-the-invaluable-2015-update.html.

Sabogal Fabio., Marin Gerardo., Otero-Sabogal Regina VanOss, Marin Barbara, and Perez-Stable Eliseo J. "Hispanic familism and acculturation: What changes and what doesn't?." Hispanic Journal of Behavioral Sciences 9. (1987): 397-412. Sage Journals. Web. 10 August 2021. https://journals.sagepub.com/doi/10.1177/07399863870094003

Sallim,AdnaanB., Sayampanathan Andrew A., Cuttilan Amit, and Ho Roger. "Prevalence of Mental Health Disorder Among Caregivers of Patients With Alzheimer Disease," Journal of the American Medical Directors Association. 16.12 (2015) :1034-41. NCIB. Web. 10 August 2021. https://pubmed.ncbi.nlm.nih.gov/26593303/

Schaeffer, Katherine. "6 facts about economic inequality in the U.S.," Washington, D.C.: Pew Research Center. 2020.

Web. 22 December 2020. https://www.pewresearch.org/fact-tank/2020/02/07/6-facts-about-economic-inequality-in-the-u-s/.

Smith, David Baarton, Feng Zhanlian, Fennell Mary L., Zinn Jacqueline S., and Vincent Mor. "Separate and unequal: Racial segregation and disparities in quality across U.S. nursing homes." Health Affairs (Milwood) 26.5 (2007): 1448-1458. NCIB. Web. 10 August 2021. https://pubmed.ncbi.nlm.nih.gov/17848457/

Stone, Lyman. "Baby Bust: Fertility is Declining the Most Among Minority Women". Charlottesville. 2018. Web. 3 January2021 https://ifstudies.org/blog/baby-bust-fertility-is-declining-the-most-among-minority-women.

Swanson, Emily, and Ricardo Alonso-Zaldivar. "AP-NORC Poll: Adult caregivers overwhelmed and undertrained". AP News. 2017. Web. 10 August 2021 https://apnews.com/article/817557c2bcd0457ab74417caef1e06ae.

The Tucker-Seeley Research Lab. "Individual Measures". University of Southern California. Web. 26 March 2021 https://gero.usc.edu/labs/tuckerseeleylab/individual-measures/.

Tucker-Seeley, Reginald. "Household financial well-being and health." Tucker-Seeley Lab. 2018. Web. 26 March 2021 https://gero.usc.edu/wp-content/uploads/2017/04/Tucker-Seeley_Summit_Slides.pdf.

U.S. Department of Labor. "Family and Medical Leave Act". DOL. Web. 3 April 2021. https://www.dol.gov/agencies/whd/fmla.

U.S. Wage and Hour Division. "Fact Sheet #28C". U.S. Department of Labor. 2015. Web. 10 August 2021. https://www.dol.gov/sites/dolgov/files/WHD/legacy/files/whdfs28C.pdf.

Made in the USA
Middletown, DE
28 November 2021